Buffy the Vampire Slayer™

The Script Book:
Season Two, Volume Two

<u>Buffy the Vampire Slayer</u>™

The Script Book:
Season Two, Volume Two

POCKET PULSE

New York   London   Toronto   Sydney   Singapore

This book is a work of fiction. Names, characters, places and incidents are products of the author's imagination or are used fictitiously. Any resemblance to actual events or locales or persons, living or dead, is entirely coincidental.

An *Original* Publication of POCKET BOOKS

 POCKET PULSE, published by
Pocket Books, a division of Simon & Schuster, Inc.
1230 Avenue of the Americas, New York, NY 10020

ISBN: 0-7434-2338-0

First Pocket Pulse trade paperback printing December 2001

10 9 8 7 6 5 4 3 2 1

POCKET PULSE and colophon are registered trademarks of Simon & Schuster, Inc.

For information regarding special discounts for bulk purchases, please contact Simon & Schuster Special Sales at 1-800-456-6798 or siness@simonandschuster.com

Printed in the U.S.A.

Historian's Note: These teleplays represent the original shooting scripts for each episode; thus we have preserved any typos and mis-attributions. The scripts may include dialogue or even full scenes that were not in the final broadcast version of the show because they were cut due to length. Also, there may be elements in the broadcast that were added at a later date.

Contents

BUFFY THE VAMPIRE SLAYER

"Lie to Me"

Written and Directed by

Joss Whedon

SHOOTING SCRIPT

September 12, 1997
September 12, 1997 (Blue Pages)
September 15, 1997 (Pink Pages)

BUFFY THE VAMPIRE SLAYER

"Lie to Me"

CAST LIST

BUFFY SUMMERS......................... Sarah Michelle Gellar
XANDER HARRIS......................... Nicholas Brendon
RUPERT GILES.......................... Anthony S. Head
WILLOW ROSENBERG...................... Alyson Hannigan
CORDELIA CHASE........................ Charisma Carpenter
ANGEL................................. David Boreanaz

JENNY CALENDAR........................*Robia La Morte
SPIKE.................................*James Marsters
DRUSILLA..............................*Juliet Landau
BILLY FORDHAM (FORD)..................*Jason Behr
DIEGO (MARVIN)........................*Jarred Paul
CHANTARELLE (JOAN)....................*Julia Lee
JAMES.................................*Will Rothhaar

BUFFY THE VAMPIRE SLAYER

"Lie to Me"

SET LIST

INTERIORS

SUNNYDALE HIGH SCHOOL
  HALL
  LIBRARY
  CLASSROOM
  SCHOOL LOUNGE

BUFFY'S HOUSE
  BUFFY'S BEDROOM
  KITCHEN
  DINING ROOM

THE BRONZE

THE FACTORY

WILLOW'S BEDROOM

THE SUNSET CLUB

EXTERIORS

SUNNYDALE HIGH SCHOOL
  *FOUNTAIN QUAD

THE BRONZE
  ALLEY BY THE BRONZE (URBAN DISTRICT)

STREET

GRAVEYARD

PLAYGROUND

BUFFY THE VAMPIRE SLAYER

"Lie to Me"

TEASER

1 EXT.   PLAYGROUND - EVENING   1

We see a little merry-go-round turning absently in the
(sorry, Gareth) foggy dark. A set of swings, also empty,
also pushed slightly by the night wind.

A jungle gym sits nearby, eight year old JAMES hanging
sullenly on it. He sits inside it, looking out at the park.

                    JAMES
          Come on, Mom...

He cranes around but there is no Mom in sight.

                    JAMES (cont'd)
          She's always late.

As he hangs, we see a figure moving slowly toward him from
behind. DRUSILLA. Her ethereal figure moves unsteadily, a
faint and senseless smile on her lips.

The boy makes her weak with hunger.

                    DRUSILLA
          Are you lost?

The boy turns, startled but not particularly scared. He
climbs out of the jungle gym, which stands between them as he
replies:

                    JAMES
          No. My Mom's supposed to pick me up
          is all.

                    DRUSILLA
          Do you want me to walk you home?

                    JAMES
          No, thank you. I'm supposed to wait.

She reaches the gym and starts coming slowly around, running
her fingers along the bars. James begins to get slightly
creeped, taking a step back.

                    JAMES (cont'd)
          'Cause my Mom is coming.

                                                    CONTINUED

> DRUSILLA
> My mummy used to sing me to sleep at
> night. "Run and catch, run and
> catch, the lamb is caught in the
> blackberry patch". She had the
> sweetest voice, like cherries. What
> will your mummy sing when they find
> your body?

Okay, now he's creeped. She is on the same side as him now,
standing still, smiling still.

> JAMES
> I'm not... I'm not supposed to talk
> to people.

> DRUSILLA
> Oh, I'm not a person, so that's
> just --

A dark figure APPEARS right before James. He jerks back,
looking up to see the dark and glowering face of ANGEL.

> ANGEL
> Run home.

James does.

Drusilla makes a whimpering growl. Angel turns to face
her -- and her face lights up.

> DRUSILLA
> My Angel.

> ANGEL
> Hello, Drusilla.

> DRUSILLA
> (comes slowly to him)
> Do you remember the song mummy used
> to sing me? Pretty. She would sing
> me to sleep, and the fairies and
> sprites would bite at my heels.

> ANGEL
> I remember.

> DRUSILLA
> Yes... you do...

CONTINUED

1 CONTINUED: (2)   1

                    ANGEL
          Drusilla, leave here. I'm offering
          you that chance. Take Spike and get
          out.

                    DRUSILLA
          Or you'll hurt me?

He looks down.

                    DRUSILLA (cont'd)
          No. No, you can't. Not anymore.

                    ANGEL
          If you don't leave... it'll go badly.
          For all of us.

                    DRUSILLA
          My dear boy's gone all away, hasn't
          he? To her.

                    ANGEL
          Who?

                    DRUSILLA
          The girl.

2 ANGLE: BUFFY   2

The girl herself, patrolling on a nearby rooftop. She spots
the two of them, looks down, uncertain.

3 ANGLE: HER POV   3

Of Angel and another woman. Too close for Buffy's comfort.
The woman puts her hand on Angel's chest.

                    DRUSILLA
          The Slayer. Your heart stinks of
          her. Poor little thing. She has no
          idea what's in store.

She stops -- actually sensing Buffy watching. She glances at
the girl, smiling to herself.

                    ANGEL
          This can't go on, Drusilla. It's
          gotta end.

                    DRUSILLA
          Oh, no, my pet...

                                        CONTINUED

3 CONTINUED: 3

She leans in for what looks to Buffy like a kiss, whispers in
Angel's ear:

                    DRUSILLA (cont'd)
          This is just the beginning.

She drifts back, away from Angel. He watches her go.

So does Buffy.

                                   BLACK OUT.

                    END OF TEASER

ACT ONE

4 INT. HALL - MORNING   4

   GILES is talking with JENNY, as they walk towards the library.

>   JENNY
>   It's a secret.
>
>   GILES
>   What kind of secret?
>
>   JENNY
>   The kind that's secret. You know,
>   where I don't tell you what it is.
>
>   GILES
>   But I just think it's customary, if
>   two people are going out of an
>   evening, for the both of them to know
>   where they're going.
>
>   JENNY
>   Oh, come on! Where's your sense of
>   adventure?
>
>   GILES
>   But, I -- how will I know what to
>   wear?
>
>   JENNY
>   (re: his tweedy look)
>   Do you own anything else?
>
>   GILES
>   Not as such.
>
>   JENNY
>   You're just gonna have to trust me,
>   Rupert.
>
>   GILES
>   All right. I put myself in your
>   hands.
>
>   JENNY
>   Now **that** sounds like fun.

An intimate moment is interrupted by:

>   BUFFY
>   Hey, guys.

CONTINUED

She approaches them -- not glum, exactly, but a tad
distracted.

                    JENNY
          I gotta take off. Tomorrow, 7:30.
          Right?

                    GILES
          Yes.

She takes off. Giles turns to Buffy and they start down the
hall.

                    GILES (cont'd)
          Did we hunt last night?

                    BUFFY
          Did a couple of quick sweeps, you
          know, downtown.

                    GILES
          No encounters?

                    BUFFY
          Nothing vampiry.

                    GILES
          Well, I've been researching our new
          friend Spike. The profile is fairly
          unappetizing -- but I still haven't
          a bead on why he's here.

                    BUFFY
          You'll figure it out.

                    GILES
          Are you all right? You seem a bit
          glum.

                    BUFFY
          I'm okay.

                    GILES
          Well, why don't you take the night
          off?

                    BUFFY
          That'd be nice.

                                              CONTINUED

4 CONTINUED: (2)   4

                        GILES
          Yes, even I realize a young person
          like yourself can't spend all her
          time fighting the forces of darkness.
          No slaying this evening. Perhaps you
          can concentrate on your homework
          instead.

She peers at him.

                        BUFFY
          Do they know about "fun" in England?

                        GILES
          Yes, but's considered very poor taste
          to have any. Very well. Do whatever
          it is you like. You could spend some
          time with Angel.

                        BUFFY
          I don't know. He might have other
          plans.

5 INT. CLASSROOM - DAY   5

6 CLOSE ON: A PIECE OF PAPER   6

Unfolded to read, in Willow's script: "Do you know who she
was?"

A WIDER ANGEL reveals the girls near the back during class.
XANDER is next to CORDELIA, who sits a bit in front, actually
participating. Buffy scribbles a reply, as Cordelia holds
forth:

                        CORDELIA
          I just don't see why everyone is
          always ragging on Marie Antoinette.
          I can so relate to her. She worked
          really hard to look that good.
          People don't appreciate that effort.

Buffy writes out: "No. Dark hair, old dress. Pretty." She
hands the note to WILLOW.

                        CORDELIA (cont'd)
          And I know, the peasants were all
          depressed.

                        XANDER
          I think you mean "oppressed."

CONTINUED

6 CONTINUED: 6

> CORDELIA
> Whatever. They were cranky. So
> they're like, "let's lose some heads
> now." Oh, that's fair. And Marie
> Antoinette cared about them. She was
> gonna let them have cake!

> TEACHER (V.O.)
> Well, that's one way to look at it...

Willow scribbles, hands back. Buffy opens to see:

"Vampire?"

Over which the BELL RINGS, signalling the end of class.

The kids rise and gather their books. Buffy turns to Willow

                                                           *

7 INT. HALL - DAY   7

                                                           *

As they exit:

> BUFFY
> I don't know. I don't think so -- I   *
> mean, they seemed pretty friendly.   *

> XANDER
> Who's friendly?   *

> BUFFY
> No one.   *

> WILLOW
> Angel and a girl.

> BUFFY
> Will, do we have to be in total share
> mode?

> XANDER
> Hey, it's **me.** If Angel's doing
> something wrong I need to know.
> 'Cause it gives me a happy

> BUFFY
> I'm glad someone has a happy.

CONTINUED

7 CONTINUED: 7

                          XANDER
               Aw, you just need cheering up. And
               I know just the thing.
                         (a few wild moves)
               Crazed dance party at the Bronze!

                                           CONTINUED

7 CONTINUED:

                    BUFFY
          I don't know.

                    XANDER
               (restrained moves)
          Very calm dance party at the Bronze.
               (no moves)
          Moping at the Bronze.

                    FORD
          I'd suggest a box of Oreos dunked in
          apple juice... but maybe she's over
          that phase.

He's standing behind Buffy, smiling. A charming and
innocuous senior, Billy Fordham, known as FORD, waits for
Buffy to turn. Which she does, wonder blossoming on her face.

                    BUFFY
          Ford?

She sees him and throws her arms around him. He gives her a
big friendly hug.

                    BUFFY (cont'd)
          Ford!

                    FORD
          Hey, Summers. How you been?

                    BUFFY
          What are you doing here?

                    FORD
          Matriculating.

                    BUFFY
          Huh?

                    FORD
          I'm finishing out my senior year at
          Sunnydale High. Dad got transferred.

                    BUFFY
          That's great!

                    FORD
          I'm glad you think so. Wasn't sure
          you'd remember me.

                                                    CONTINUED

7 CONTINUED: (2)

                    BUFFY
          Remember you? Duh, we were in school
          together for seven years. You were
          my giant fifth grade crush. Remember.

                    XANDER
          So, you two know each other?

                    BUFFY
          Oh! I'm sorry. This is Ford. Uh,
          Billy Fordham. This is Xander and
          Willow.

                    XANDER
          Hi.

                    FORD
          Hey.

                    WILLOW
          Nice to meet you.

                    BUFFY
          Ford and I went to Hemery together,
          in L.A.
                    (to Ford)
          And you're here? For real?

                    FORD
          Dad got the transfer, boom -- just
          dragged me out of Hemery and put me
          down here.

                    BUFFY
          This is great! I mean, It's hard,
          sudden move, all your friends,
          delicate time very emotional but
          let's talk about me this is great!

                    WILLOW
          So you guys were sweeties in fifth
          grade?

                    BUFFY
          Not even. Ford wouldn't give me the
          time of day.

                    FORD
          Well, I was a manly sixth grader,
          couldn't be bothered with someone
          that young.

                                              CONTINUED

                    BUFFY
          It was terrible. I moped over you
          for months. Sitting in my room
          listening to that Divinyls song, "I
          touch myself".
                    (suddenly sheepish)
          Of course, I had no idea what it was
          about.

                    WILLOW
          It's fun to meet someone who knew
          Buffy from before she was the --
                    (off Buffy's glare)
          -- the here-being girl.

                    XANDER
                    (less enthused)
          Yeah, it's fun.

                    BUFFY
          Hey! Are you busy tonight?

                    FORD
          I'm hoping you'll tell me that I am.

                    BUFFY
          We're going to the Bronze. It's the
          local club and you gotta come.

                    FORD
          I'd love to, but if you guys had
          plans -- would I be imposing?

                    XANDER
          Only in the literal sense.

                    BUFFY
          You're coming. I have spoken.

                    FORD
          Okay, then. I gotta find the
          admissions office, get my papers in
          order.

                    BUFFY
          I'll walk you. See you guys in French.

                    FORD
          Good meeting you.

They take off, Xander watching them go as Willow works
something out in her head.

CONTINUED

7 CONTINUED: (4)   7

                    XANDER
"This is Ford, my bestest friend of
all my friends". Jeez. Didn't she
know any fat guys?

                    WILLOW
                  (gets it)
Oh! **That's** what that song's about?

8 INT. BRONZE - NIGHT   8

The usual suspects mill about, dance, talk. Cordelia is on
the dance floor, rockin' out.

Buffy enters, cranes about for her peoples. She spots them
on a couch. Ford is with them already, talking, making
Willow laugh and Xander smile politely. Buffy crosses to
them.

                    BUFFY
Hey, you got here.

                    FORD
Wasn't hard to find.

                    WILLOW
Buffy, Ford was just telling us about
the ninth grade beauty contest. And
the, uh, swimsuit competition?

                    BUFFY
Oh, God. Ford! Stop that! The more
people you tell about it, the more
people I have to kill.

                    FORD
You can't touch me, Summers. I know
all your darkest secrets.

                    XANDER
Care to make a small wager on that?

                    BUFFY
I'm gonna grab a soda. Ford, try not
to talk.

She crosses to the bar. As she arrives the man in front
turns to go, drink in hand. It's Angel.

                    BUFFY (cont'd)
Oh!

                                              CONTINUED

8 CONTINUED: 8

                          ANGEL
          Hey. I was hoping you'd show.

                          BUFFY
          You drink? Drinks? I mean, non-
          blood things.

                          ANGEL
          Yeah. I eat, too. Not for
          nutritional value -- it just kind of
          passes the time.

                          BUFFY
          Oh. Who knew.

                          ANGEL
          There's a lot about me you don't know.

                          BUFFY
          I believe that.

9 ANGEL: WILLOW, XANDER AND FORD   9

     Look over at the two of them.

                          WILLOW
          That's Angel.

                          XANDER
          He's Buffy's beau. Her special
          friend.

                          FORD
          He's not in school, right? He looks
          older than her.

                          XANDER
          You're not wrong.

10 ANGLE: BUFFY AND ANGEL   10

                          BUFFY
          So, what'd you do last night?

                          ANGEL
          Nothing.

                          BUFFY
          Nothing at all? You ceased to exist?

                          ANGEL
          No, I mean I stayed in. Read.

CONTINUED

                         BUFFY
              Oh.

Her face hardens at the lie. She turns and joins her friends.

                         FORD
              Didn't want that soda after all?

                         BUFFY
              Not that thirsty.

Angel has come up behind her.

                         WILLOW
              Hey, Angel.

                         FORD
              Hi.

                         BUFFY
              This is Ford. We went to school
              together in L.A.

They shake hands.

                         ANGEL
              Nice to meet you.

                         FORD
              Whoah. Cold hands.

                         XANDER
              You're not wrong.

                         ANGEL
              So, you're visiting Buffy?

                         FORD
              No, I'm actually here to stay. Just
              moved down.

                         XANDER
              Well, Sunnydale is a fun town to live
              in. If you're a small patch of moss.

                         WILLOW
              Angel, do you want to sit?

                         BUFFY
              It's so crowded in here. I'm hot.
                   (to Ford.)
              Do you want to go for a walk?

                                                    CONTINUED

10 CONTINUED: (2)

                         FORD
                Uh, sure. That'd be nice.

They rise. Angel steps back for them to pass.

                         BUFFY
                I'll see you all tomorrow.

                         ANGEL
                Good night.

                         FORD
                Take care.

Awkward silence follows this awkward scene.

                         XANDER
                Okay, once more, with tension.

Cordelia joins the group, eyes on the departing figures.

                         CORDELIA
                Who's the tasty treat?

                         XANDER
                Buffy's oldest and dearest.

                         ANGEL
                He just moved here?

                         XANDER
                Yeah. And boy, does he move fast.

Not what Angel wanted to hear.

                         WILLOW
                Well, Angel, you can still hang with
                us --

But he's gone.

                         WILLOW (cont'd)
                      (to Xander)
                See? You made him do that thing
                where he's gone.

11 EXT. ALLEY - NIGHT   11

     As Buffy and Ford walk, not talking just now. After a bit:

                         FORD
                So, that was your boyfriend?

                                                          CONTINUED

11 CONTINUED: 11

> BUFFY
> No. Well, yeah. Well, maybe. Let's
> lay off the tough questions for a
> while.

> FORD
> Sorry. So, what else do you do for
> fun around here?

As he is saying this, Buffy hears a SCUFFLE around the
corner. She grabs Ford.

> BUFFY
> Um, Uh, my purse! I left it at the
> Bronze. Would you get it for me?
> Thanks.

> FORD
> Uh, okay.

> BUFFY
> Good. Run. Thanks.

Confused, he starts off. Buffy runs around the corner.

12 ANGLE: FORD   12

Stops, turns back. What going on here? He starts moving
slowly toward the alley.

The SOUNDS of fighting emerge. Then a woman emerges, running
away in terror. Ford keeps inching closer - as a trash can
emerges on the fly. Just misses him.

He turns the corner to see:

13 ANGLE: BUFFY   13

As she stakes a vampire. He turns to dust right in front of
Ford's eyes. Buffy turns, is startled.

> BUFFY
> Oh! You're back.

> FORD
> What's going on?

> BUFFY
> There was a cat. A cat here and then
> there was, another cat. And they
> fought, the cats, and then they left.

CONTINUED

13 CONTINUED:

                    FORD
          Oh. I thought you were just slaying
          a vampire.

                    BUFFY
          What? Whatting a what?

                    FORD
          I know, Buffy. You don't have to
          lie. I've been trying to figure out
          the right time to tell you. I know
          you're the Slayer.

Off Buffy's look:

14 INT. WILLOW'S BEDROOM - NIGHT

She is on the phone.

                    WILLOW
          Just like that? He told you?

                                        INTERCUT WITH:

15 INT. BUFFY'S KITCHEN - CONTINUOUS - NIGHT

Buffy is on the cordless, sitting on the counter.

                    BUFFY
          Just like that. Said he found out
          right before I got booted from Hemery.

                    WILLOW
          Wow. It's neat. Is it neat?

                    UBFFY
          It... yeah, I guess it is. It's nice
          to have someone else that I can open
          up to. Just be myself. No more
          hiding.

16 EXT. URBAN DISTRICT - NIGHT

(Okay, it's our damn alley.) Ford walks cheerfully along.
Comes to a door in what appears to be a pretty rundown
building. Over the large metal door is a painted sign: no
words, just a picture of a setting sun.

Ford pounds on the door. A little window in the center
slides open. A GUY of about 25 -- strong, tattooed and
suspicious, peers out.

CONTINUED

16 CONTINUED: 16

The little window slides closed -- and the door opens. Ford
enters:

17 INT. HALL - CONTINUOUS - NIGHT   17

A small hall, painted black and leading to another, even
heavier metal door.

18 INT. THE SUNSET CLUB - CONTINUOUS - NIGHT   18

And he's in another world. The Sunset Club is dark, fairly   *
Goth, and very lively. It's like a giant underground bunker
done up for permanent Halloween. The door opens onto a
balcony that rings the top of the large space. There is a
bridge of metal grillwork that spans the space up here as
well, and steps leading down into the main floor, which
divides into various lounge spaces, dance areas, and small
private rooms.

There's maybe thirty people here, all corsets and velvet and
black lipstick.

The MUSIC is loud and pulsing. Lights flicker and swirl
across Ford's face as he looks about him.

19 ANGLE: WELDER GUY.   19

He's got black hair, black lips, and dark goggles on as he
works on the metal door hinge, crouching in a shower of
sparks.

Ford nods at him (we cannot tell exactly what the man is
doing), then starts down the stairs. As he reaches the
bottom he is accosted by DIEGO, a true vampire wannabe. His
ruffled shirt and velvet cape only accentuate his nerdliness.
If this group has a leader, Diego is it.

                    DIEGO
          Ford. Ford!

                    FORD
          Hey.

As always, Ford is fairly dismissive of Diego.

                    DIEGO
          Well? How did it go?

                    FORD
          Went good.

                    DIEGO
          Good? That's it? Well, when --

                                                    CONTINUED

                         FORD
          Soon.

                         DIEGO
          You know, you could give me a little
          more information here. I'm trusting
          you, I'm out on a limb here -- not to
          mention the lease is almost up on
          this place and who's gonna cover
          that, my dad's not sending me another
          dime --

                         FORD
          Marvin --

                         DIEGO
          Diego. Come on, it's Diego now.

                         FORD
          Diego. Ridilin. Everything's gonna
          be fine.

A slinky goth girl, CHANTARELLE (formerly Joan), glides up to
the boys with a couple of goblets. Ford takes one. He pops
open a prescription bottle and washes down a pill, then
continues:

                         FORD (cont'd)
          Just make sure you're ready when I
          say. True believers only.

                         CHANTARELLE
          I can't wait.

Ford's attention is caught by the movie playing against a
nearby wall. It's on a vid monitor -- and on another behind
Ford. Ford seems mesmerized as he sips from the goblet.

                         DIEGO
          Well, I still think I should be in on
          the plan.

                         FORD
                    (eyes on the movie)
          Diego, you gotta trust me. A couple
          more days and we'll get to do the two
          things every American teen should
          have the chance to do. Die young...

He turns to Diego and Chantarelle, smiling.

                         FORD (cont'd)
          ... and stay pretty.

19 CONTINUED: (2)

He turns back to the movie. Watches, mouthing every line as
it's spoken. We see him and the second vid screen behind
him, as both he and Jack Palance intone:

                    FORD\JACK PALANCE
          So, you play your wits against mine.
          Me, who commanded armies hundreds of
          years before you were born. Fools!
          There is no way in this life to stop
          me...

                                        BLACK OUT.

          END OF ACT ONE

ACT TWO

20 INT. WILLOW'S BEDROOM - NIGHT   20

Willow comes out of the bathroom, brushing her hair out. She
passes the french doors -- and starts, as she sees Angel
standing behind them.

              WILLOW
    Oh! Angel.

She looks over at her door, slightly open -- no parent
noises -- then opens one of the French doors.

              WILLOW (cont'd)
    What are you doing here?

              ANGEL
    I wanted to talk to you.

              WILLOW
    Well, oh.

She pulls the door all the way open, waits for him to step in.

              WILLOW (cont'd)
    Well?

              ANGEL
    I can't... unless you invite me. I
    can't come in.

              WILLOW
    Oh! Okay. Uh, I invite you. To
    come in.

He does. Willow goes over to her bed. She spots her bra
lying on it. In a panic, she stuffs it under her pillow.
Turns to him.

              ANGEL
    If this is a bad time...

              WILLOW
    No, I just... I'm not supposed to
    have boys in my room.

And she clearly hasn't, by her nervous demeanor.

              ANGEL
    Well, I promise to behave myself.

CONTINUED

                      WILLOW
          Okay, good.

                      ANGEL
          I guess I need help. And you're the
          first person I thought of.

                      WILLOW
          Help? You mean like on homework?
          No, 'cause you're old and you already
          know stuff.

                      ANGEL
          I want you to track someone down. On
          the net.

                      WILLOW
          Oh! Great. I'm **so** the net girl.

She crosses to her desk, boots up.

                      ANGEL
          I just want to find everything I can.
          Records, affiliates -- I'm not even
          sure what I'm looking for yet.

                      WILLOW
          What's the name?

                      ANGEL
          Billy Fordham.

She stops. Then, typing, says:

                      WILLOW
          Uh, Angel, if I say something you
          don't really wanna hear, do you
          promise not to bite me?

                      ANGEL
          Are you gonna tell me that I'm
          jealous?

                      WILLOW
          Well, you do sometimes get that way.

                      ANGEL
          You know, I never used to.

He sits on the bed behind her.

                                CONTINUED

>   ANGEL (cont'd)
>   Things used to be pretty simple. A
>   hundred years just hanging out,
>   feeling guilty. I really honed my
>   brooding skills. Then she comes
>   along... Yeah, I get jealous. But
>   I know people and my gut tells me
>   this is a wrong guy.

>   WILLOW
>   Okay, well, you've got a smart gut I
>   guess. But if there isn't anything
>   weird -- hey, that's weird.

He rises, comes behind her.

>   ANGEL
>   What?

>   WILLOW
>   I just checked the school records.
>   He's not in them. Usually they
>   transfer your grades and stuff,
>   but... he's not even registered.

She starts typing fast.

>   ANGEL
>   He said he was in school with you
>   guys, right?

>   WILLOW
>   Okay, there's no Fordham listed in
>   Sunnydale. Curiouser and Curiouser.
>   Let me see if I can --

>   WILLOW'S MOM (O.S.)
>   Willow? Are you still up?

>   WILLOW
>   Ack! Go!

He glides to the French doors, Willow up to close them.

>   WILLOW (cont'd)
>   (calls out:)
>   I'm just going to bed now, Mom. I'm
>   very sleepy.
>   (to Angel)
>   Come by at sunset tomorrow. I'll
>   keep looking.

CONTINUED

20 CONTINUED: (3)   20

                    ANGEL
          Don't tell Buffy what we're doing,
          all right?

                    WILLOW
          You want me to lie to her? It's
          Buffy. Besides, I don't lie good.
          I lie bad.

                    ANGEL
          Just don't bring it up. 'Til we know
          what's what.

                    WILLOW
          Okay. It's probably nothing.

                    ANGEL
          That'd be nice.

21 EXT. SCHOOL - FOUNTAIN QUAD - DAY   21   *

     Buffy and Ford are sitting and talking.

                    BUFFY
          And then everything was Vampires. I
          slacked utterly in school -- and my
          social life pretty much dried up and
          blew away.

                    FORD
          You made quite a hit at the prom.

                    BUFFY
          Oh, God, the prom. What a disaster.

                    FORD
          Wasn't dull, though. Watching the
          gym go up in flames... it was like a
          movie. Life isn't nearly enough like
          a movie, don't you think?

                    BUFFY
          I think that was the worst night of
          my life.

                    FORD
          You saved a lot of people's lives.
          I know it - I bet there's others who
          do too.

                                                    CONTINUED

21   CONTINUED: 21

                    BUFFY
          It's good to hear. And it's good to
          be able to talk to someone who knows.
          Who knew me before, and... well,
          during.

                    FORD
          You know, one minute you're a kid,
          living in your safe kid world, and
          then -- Truth hits you in the face.
          Vampires. I'll never forget that
          night.

     BELL RINGS. They get up and head inside.

22   OMITTED   22   *

                    BUFFY
          Most everybody else did.

                    FORD
          What's up with that? Nobody would
          say a word.

                    BUFFY
          People ignore truths they don't like.

     Cordelia comes up to them, all smiles.

                    CORDELIA
          Buffy, you haven't introduced me to
          your new friend.

                    BUFFY
          Yeah, isn't that weird?

     She blows by her, Ford in tow.

                    FORD
          Who is that?

                    BUFFY
          A truth I like to ignore.

A23 INT. SCHOOL LOUNGE - DAY   A23   *

                                                                       *
     Buffy and Ford enter, pass Willow.

                    BUFFY
          Will! What's up?

                                                    CONTINUED

A23 CONTINUED: A23

                    WILLOW
          Nothing.

                                              CONTINUED

She's a little jumpy, afraid of being found out.

                    BUFFY
          You wanna hang? We were cafeteria
          bound.

                    WILLOW
          I'm going to work in the computer
          lab. On school work that I have. So
          I could not hang just now. Hi Ford.

                    FORD
          Morning.

                    BUFFY
          Okay, Will. Fess up.

                    WILLOW
                (scared)
          What?

                    BUFFY
          Were you drinking coffee again?
          'Cause we've talked about this.

                    WILLOW
          Ha ha ha ha!
                (to Ford)
          It makes me jumpy.
                (to both)
          I have to go. Away.

She does.

                    FORD
          Nice girl.

                    BUFFY
          There aren't two of those in the
          world.

Giles approaches.

                    GILES
          Buffy. Ms. Calendar and I are
          going... somewhere... tonight. She's
          given me her beeper number in case
          you need me for any...
                (glances at Ford)
          ... study help. Suddenly.

                    BUFFY
          He knows, Giles.

CONTINUED

22 CONTINUED: (2)   22

                         GILES
               What?

                         BUFFY
               Ford. He knows I'm the Slayer.

                         FORD
               I know.

                         GILES
               Oh. Very good then.
                    (pulls Buffy aside)
               Buffy, you aren't by any chance
               giving away your secret identity just
               to impress cute boys, are you?

She smiles.

                         BUFFY
               I didn't tell him. He knew.

                         GILES
               All right. Well, remember, if you
               need me --

                         BUFFY
               Go. Experience this thing called
               fun. I'll try not to have a crisis.

23 EXT. FRONT OF SCHOOL - NIGHT   23

Buffy and Ford have been walking together for a while.

                         BUFFY
               And on your right, once again -- the
               beautiful campus. You've now seen
               pretty much everything there is to
               see in Sunnydale.

                         FORD
               Well, it's really ...

                         BUFFY
               Feel free to say 'dull'.

                         FORD
               Okay. Dull works.

Buffy spots something out of the corner of her eye:

24 ANGLE: TWO VAMPS   24

are sneaking towards the administration building.

CONTINUED

24 CONTINUED: 24

Ford follows Buffy's gaze and sees them.

                    FORD
          Or maybe not so dull... Is that more
          vampires?

                    BUFFY
          Must be the weather.

She pulls a stake and a cross out of her pocket, hands Ford
the cross. He produces a rather hastily carved stake of his
own from his pocket.

                    BUFFY (cont'd)
          Stick close to me.

She sneaks toward the building, up the stairs, toward the
corner. Looks around. There are no vampires to be seen.

                    FORD
          Maybe they were just passing through.

                    BUFFY
          I don't think so.

The smaller vampire, JULIA, JUMPS Buffy from the bushes.
Buffy easily throws her, but the second much bigger vampire,
LEAPS OUT and takes Buffy over the balcony.

25 ANGLE: JULIA   25

lays on the ground catching her breath, when Ford JUMPS on
her. He holds the stake to her chest, the cross to her face.

                    FORD
          You've got one chance to live. Tell
          me what I want to know, and I let you
          go.

26 ANGLE: BUFFY   26

as she takes out the bigger vamp. Having done so, she crests
the stairs to find Ford, all alone. He is breathing hard,
winded.

                    BUFFY
          Where's the other one?

                    FORD
          I killed her.
               (he coughs)
          I killed her and she just turned to
          dust. It was amazing.

                                                        CONTINUED

26 CONTINUED: 26

Off his gleeful smile we cut to:

27 EXT. URBAN DISTRICT - NIGHT   27

Willow, Angel and Xander head for the Sunset Club.

                    WILLOW
          The only thing I could track down
          were some E-mails to a guy called
          Diego. And this address. The Sunset
          Club. I still didn't find anything
          incriminating.

                    ANGEL
          He leaves no paper trail, no records.
          That's incriminating enough.

                    XANDER
          I'm gonna have to go with Dead Boy on
          this one.

                    ANGEL
          Could you not call me that?

Angel knocks on the door. The little window slides open.

                    ANGEL (cont'd)
          We're friends of Ford's. He said we
          should come by.

A beat, then the window slides shut. The door opens.

28 INT. THE HALL - CONTINUED - NIGHT   28

The three file in, head for the big iron door. Door Guy
watches them suspiciously.

They enter:

29 INT. SUNSET CLUB - NIGHT   29

Same crowd, same beat. Xander, Willow and Angel stand at the
entrance, taking it in.

                    WILLOW
          Boy, we blend right in.

                    XANDER
          In no way do we stick out like a sore
          thumb.

CONTINUED

29 CONTINUED: 29

                    ANGEL
          Let's look around. You guys check
          out downstairs.

                    XANDER
          Sure thing, Bossy the cow.

He and Willow start down the stairs as Angel makes his way
around the balcony.

                    WILLOW
          Okay, but do they really stick out?

                    XANDER
          What?

                    WILLOW
          Sore thumbs. Do they stick out? I
          mean, have you ever seen a thumb and
          gone "wow, that baby is **sore**".

                    XANDER
          You have too many thoughts

30 ANGLE: ANGEL   30

     Makes his way around upstairs, looking about with increasing
     suspicion.

31 ANGLE: XANDER AND WILLOW   31

     Cruise about downstairs.

                    XANDER
          Okay, are we noticing a theme here?

                    WILLOW
          Like, as in, "Vampires Yay"?

                    XANDER
          That's the one.

Chantarelle approaches them.

                    CHANTARELLE
          You guys are newbies, I can tell.

                    WILLOW
          Oh, no. We come here all the time.

                    XANDER
          My corset's just at the cleaners.

                                              CONTINUED

31 CONTINUED:

> CHANTARELLE
> Don't be ashamed. It's cool that
> you're open to it. We welcome anyone
> who's interested in the Lonely Ones.

> WILLOW
> The Lonely Ones?

> ANGEL
> Vampires.

He's come up to them, not looking particularly amused.

> XANDER
> Oh. We usually call them the nasty
> pointy bitey ones.

> CHANTARELLE
> So many people have that
> misconception. But they who walk
> with the night are not interested in
> harming anyone. They're separate
> from humanity, and must carry the
> burden of immortality. They are
> creatures above us. Exalted.

> ANGEL
> You're a fool.

Even his companions are thrown by the harshness of his tone.

> CHANTARELLE
> You don't have to be so
> confrontational about it. Other
> viewpoints than yours may be valid,
> you know.

Chantarelle wanders off, hurt.

> WILLOW
> Nice meeting you...

> XANDER
>   (to Angel)
> Boy, you're really a people person.

> WILLOW
> Nobody's gonna talk to us now.

> ANGEL
> I've seen enough. And I've seen this
> type before.
>   (more)

CONTINUED

                    ANGEL (cont'd)
          They're children, making up bedtime
          stories about friendly vampires to
          comfort themselves in the dark.

                    WILLOW
          Is that so bad? I mean the dark can
          get pretty dark, sometimes you need
          a story.

                    ANGEL
          These people don't know anything
          about vampires. What they are, how
          they live, how they dress...

The moment he says that a club member walks by in THE EXACT
SAME OUTFIT that Angel is wearing. Angel looks sheepish for
a moment as Xander and Willow eye him sardonically.

                    XANDER
          You know, I love a good diatribe, but
          I'm still curious why Ford, the
          bestest friend of the Slayer, is
          hanging with a bunch of vampire
          wannabe's.

                    WILLOW
          Something's up with him.
               (to Angel)
          You were right about that.

32 INT. LIBRARY - NIGHT   32

     Giles and Jenny enter with Buffy.

                    BUFFY
          Sorry to beep you guys in the middle
          of stuff, but this did seem a bit
          weird.

                    GILES
          No, you did the right thing.
          Absolutely.

                    JENNY
               (to Giles)
          You hated it that much?

                    GILES
          No! But -- vampires on campus --
          there could be implications... very
          grave...

                                                      CONTINUED

                    JENNY
Why didn't you say something?

                    GILES
No, honestly, I've always been
interested in... monster trucks. I
swear.

                    BUFFY
You took him to monster trucks?

                    JENNY
I thought it would be a change.

                    GILES
It was a change.

                    JENNY
We could have just left.

                    GILES
And miss the nitro burning funny
cars? Couldn't have that. Best part.

                    BUFFY
Okay, can we get back on the vampire
tip? These guys were here with a
purpose.

                    GILES
And we have to figure out what that
purpose is.

                    JENNY
Where's your friend?

                    BUFFY
I sent him home.

                    GILES
Good. The less he's mixed up in
this, the safer he'll be.

                    BUFFY
Well, he did bag a vamp his first
time out. You gotta give him credit
for... that...

Something on the table catches her eye.

                    JENNY
Something wrong?

                                       CONTINUED

32 CONTINUED: (2)   32

                         BUFFY
               Who is this?   *

                                                                     *

She picks up an old DAGUERREOTYPE portrait which has been   *
stuck between the pages of a book.   *

                                                                     *

                         GILES
               She's called Drusilla. A sometime
               paramour or Spike's.

                         BUFFY
               Not sometime. Nowtime.

                         GILES
               She was reported killed by an angry
               mob in Prague.

                         BUFFY
               Well, they don't make angry mobs like
               they used to cuz this girl's alive.
               I saw her with Angel.

                         GILES
               With Angel?

                         JENNY
               Isn't he supposed to be a good guy?

                         BUFFY
                    (quietly, as the
                     implication sinks in)
               Yes. He is.

                         JENNY
               I think maybe we need to read up on
               this nice lady.

Giles crosses to his office.

                         GILES
               Some of my newer volumes might be
               helpful. My own research has --

Vampire Julia JUMPS at him as he nears the door. She has an
old book in her hands.

                                                        CONTINUED

32 CONTINUED: (3)   32

She grabs him and hurls him into Buffy, knocking her down.
She races to the back, leaping first on the table and then to
the balcony, disappearing into the stacks. Buffy stares
after her as Giles gets up.

                    JENNY
          You guys okay?

                    GILES
          A book. It took one of my books.

                    JENNY
          Well at least someone in this school
          is reading...

                    BUFFY
          He said he killed it.
                    (turns to them)
          That's the vampire Ford said he
          killed.

                    GILES
          He lied?

A beat, as it sinks in.

                    BUFFY
          Why?

                                              CUT TO:

33 INT. THE FACTORY - NIGHT   33

Drusilla is talking softly to something. We pull back to
reveal a birdcage...

                    DRUSILLA
          You sing the sweetest little song.
          Won't you sing for me? Don't you
          love me anymore?

...and an entirely dead bird lying on the bottom.

SPIKE comes up behind her.

                    SPIKE
          Darling, I heard a funny thing just
          now. Lucius tells me you went out
          for a hunt the other night.

                                              CONTINUED

33 CONTINUED: 33

                          DRUSILLA
                    (focussed on the bird)
               My tummy was growly. And you were
               out.
                    (to the bird)
               Come on. I will pout if you don't
               sing...

                          SPIKE
               You, uh, run into anyone? Anyone
               interesting?
                    (she doesn't answer)
               Like Angel?

                          DRUSILLA
               Angel.

                          SPIKE
               Yeah. What might you guys have to
               talk about then? Old times?
               Childhood pranks? It's a little off,
               you two so friendly, him being the
               enemy and all that.

                          DRUSILLA
                    (to the bird)
               I'll give you a seed if you sing...

                          SPIKE
                    (losing patience)
               The bird's dead, Dru. You left it in
               the cage and you didn't feed it and
               now it's all dead. Just like the
               last one.

She makes that noise she makes when she's unhappy and may
cry. He softens instantly, wrapping his arms around her.

                          SPIKE (cont'd)
               I'm sorry, baby. I'm a bad, rude
               man. I just don't like you going
               out. You are weak. Would you like
               a new bird? One that's not dead?

                          FORD
               This is so cool!

Spike spins, murder on his (NOW VAMPIRE) face. Other
vampires gather, menacing.

                                                      CONTINUED

                        FORD (cont'd)
          I would totally live here.
                    (points to rolly ramp)
          Do you ever slide down that thing?
          I bet you do.

                        SPIKE
          Do I have anyone on watch here? It's
          called security, people. Are you all
          asleep?

He crosses to Ford, a smile working across his lips.

                        SPIKE (cont'd)
          Or did we finally find a restaurant
          that delivers.

Ford, for all his bravado, is clearly nervous -- and clearly
high on that adrenaline.

                        FORD
          I know who you are.

                        SPIKE
          Yeah, I know who I am, too. So what?

                        FORD
          I came looking for you. Spike. You
          are Spike, right? William the Bloody?

                        SPIKE
          You've got a real death wish. It's
          almost interesting.

Vampire Julia enters with the book. Spike sees, signals for
her to come over. He takes the book, leafs through it.

                        SPIKE (cont'd)
          This is great. This will be very
          useful.
                    (not looking up)
          So, how'd you find me?

Julia looks at Ford in fear. She's dead if he gives it away.

                        FORD
          That doesn't matter. I've got
          something to offer you.

Spike looks up, lays the book on a table.

CONTINUED

>   FORD (cont'd)
> I'm pretty sure this is the part
> where you take out a watch and say
> I've got thirty seconds to convince
> you not to kill me. It's traditional.

>   SPIKE
> Well, I don't go much for tradition.

He grabs Ford and moves to bite -- Ford's eyes widen with
fear -- but a hand on Spike's shoulder stops him. It's Dru.

>   DRUSILLA
> Wait, sweetie.

He stops, stares at Ford. Lets go.

>   SPIKE
> Well?

>   FORD
> Come on. Say it. It's no fun if you
> don't say it.

>   SPIKE
> What? Oh.
>   (rolls his eyes,
>   then, very flatly:)
> You've got thirty seconds to convince
> me not to kill you.

>   FORD
> Yes! This is the best. I wanna be
> like you. A vampire.

>   SPIKE
> I've known you for two minutes and I
> can't stand you. I don't really
> feature you living forever.
>   (to Dru)
> Can I eat him now, love?

>   FORD
> Well, feature this. I'm offering a
> trade. You make me a vampire. And
> I give you the Slayer.

He has their attention.

                                        BLACK OUT.

                    END OF ACT TWO

ACT THREE

34 INT BUFFY'S KITCHEN - NIGHT   34

Buffy is making a mug of cocoa in the kitchen when Angel
appears at the door.

                    ANGEL
          Buffy. May I come in?

                    BUFFY
          Sure. I thought once you'd been
          invited you could always just walk in.

                    ANGEL
          I can. I was being polite.

                    BUFFY
          Oh.

                    ANGEL
          We need to talk.

                    BUFFY
          Do we?

                    ANGEL
          It's about your friend Ford. He's
          not what he seems.

                    BUFFY
          Well, who is these days?

                    ANGEL
          Willow ran him down on the computer.

                    BUFFY
          Willow?

She turns and crosses into:

35 INT. DINING ROOM - CONTINUOUS - NIGHT   35

where her homework is laid out. She puts the cocoa down as
Angel follows her in.

                    ANGEL
          We found this address. We checked it
          out with Xander and it turned out
          to --

CONTINUED

                         BUFFY
          And Xander? Wow, everybody's in.
          It's a great big exciting conspiracy.

                         ANGEL
          What are you talking about?

                         BUFFY
          I'm talking about the people I trust.
          Who's Drusilla?

Angel's face falls.

                         BUFFY (cont'd)
          And don't lie to me. I'm tired of it.

                         ANGEL
          Some lies are necessary.

                         BUFFY
          For what?

                         ANGEL
          Sometimes the truth is worse. You
          live long enough, you find that out.

                         BUFFY
          I can take it. I can take the truth.

                         ANGEL
          Do you love me?

                         BUFFY
          What?

                         ANGEL
          Do you?

                         BUFFY
          I love you. I don't know if I trust
          you.

                         ANGEL
          Maybe you shouldn't do either.

                         BUFFY
          Maybe I'm the one should decide.

He waits a beat. Then:

                                                  CONTINUED

35 CONTINUED: (2)   35

                    ANGEL
          I did a lot of unconscionable things
          when I became a Vampire. Drusilla
          was the worst. She was... an
          obsession of mine. She was pure, and
          sweet and chaste.

                    BUFFY
          You made her a vampire.

                    ANGEL
          First I made her insane. Killed
          everyone she loved, visited every
          mental torture on her I could devise.
          She eventually fled to a convent and
          the day she took her holy orders I
          turned her into a demon.

For a moment Buffy can't say a thing. Can't even look at him,

                    BUFFY
          Well, I asked for the truth...

                    ANGEL
          Ford's part of some society that
          reveres vampires. Practically
          worships them. I don't know what he
          wants from you. But you can't trust
          him.

Off her stare we cut to:

36 EXT. SCHOOL - FOUNTAIN QUAD - DAY   36   *

Buffy walks along, alone with her thoughts, till she sees
Ford coming. She steels herself.

                    FORD
          Buffy!

                    BUFFY
          Ford.

She tries to smile. His own smile seems suddenly predatory,
cold. The CAMERA circles them as they talk.

                    FORD
          I had a great time last night. Well,
          an interesting time.

                    BUFFY
          I'm glad.

                                                    CONTINUED

36 CONTINUED:

                          FORD
          I'm probably presumptuous here but do
          you want to go out again tonight?

                          BUFFY
          I'm not busy.

                          FORD
          I sort of had an idea. It's a
          secret - I kind of want to surprise
          you.

                          BUFFY
          I like surprises.

                          FORD
          Cool. You know that place you were
          telling me about, the burger joint
          that got condemned? Can you meet me
          there?

                          BUFFY
          Sure.

                          FORD
          At nine?

                          BUFFY
          At nine.

                          FORD
          It's gonna be fun.

He takes off. Buffy watches him.

37 INT. SCHOOL LOUNGE - DAY   37

    Cordelia sits with Xander and Willow, pressing them.

                          CORDELIA
          Come on, can't you tell me anything
          about him?

                          WILLOW
          Why are you so interested in Ford?

                          CORDELIA
          In case you haven't noticed there is
          a devastating cute guy shortage right
          now.
                             (more)

CONTINUED

37 CONTINUED: 37

                    CORDELIA (cont'd)
          The government is calling for
          rationing so why does Buffy get to
          horde them all? She has Angel. So   *
          come on, what's Ford interested in?

                    XANDER
          Vampires.

                    CORDELIA
                 (deflated)
          Oh great. That's Buffy's best
          subject. You sure he doesn't like
          clothes?

Buffy enters. Her friends accost her.   *

                    WILLOW
          Hey Buffy. Did, uh, Angel -

                    BUFFY
          He told me. Everything.

Her voice is pretty cold. Willow looks down.

                    WILLOW
          I'm sorry we kept stuff from you.

                    BUFFY
                 (almost means it)
          It's okay.

                    WILLOW
          When Angel came to my room he was
          just really concerned for you. And
          we didn't want to say anything in
          case we were wrong.

Buffy softens - puts her hand on Willow's arm.

                    XANDER
          Did you find out what Ford is up to?

                    BUFFY
          I will.

She takes off. They watch her go. After a beat:

                    XANDER
          Angel was in your _bedroom_?

                                        CONTINUED

37 CONTINUED: (2)   37

                         WILLOW
                        (nods)
            Ours is a forbidden love.

38 INT. THE SUNSET CLUB - AFTERNOON   38

    There are only twelve or so people here now -- the True
    Believers. Ford enters, goes down to Chantarelle.

                         FORD
            Chantarelle. Is everything ready?

                         DIEGO
                        (approaching)
            Of course it's ready, I took care of
            it. I always take care of it.

                         CHANTARELLE
            Is it time? Tonight?

                         FORD
            Are you nervous?

                         CHANTARELLE
            Yes. No. I'm ready for the change.
            Do you really think they'll bless us?

                         FORD
            I know they will. Everything's
            falling into place.

                         DIEGO
            What about your friends? Are they
            coming? I don't think it's fair --
            they're not true believers.

                         FORD
            What are you talking about?

                         DIEGO
            Your friends. They came last night.
            Two guys and a girl.

                         CHANTARELLE
            One was mean.

                         DIEGO
            That's not the point. They weren't
            even dressed right. Plus they didn't
            know the password so officially they
            really shouldn't have been here.

                                           CONTINUED

                    FORD
          Oh, Christ. Why didn't you tell me
          about this?

                    DIEGO
          I have to do everything, okay Mister
          flawless plan guy? So maybe it
          slipped my mind.

                    CHANTARELLE
               (worried)
          It's gonna be all right, isn't it?
          They're not gonna let us down?

                    FORD
          It's gonna be fine.

                    CHANTARELLE
          I need them to bless me.

                    FORD
          It's gonna be **fine.**

                    BUFFY
          It's really not.

They turn to see her coming down the steps. Door Guy is a
few steps above her, nursing a hurt nose. Ford's face
hardens upon seeing her. He glances at Diego.

                    FORD
          It's kind of drafty in here.

Diego sidles off as Buffy approaches.

                    BUFFY
          I'm sorry, Ford, I just couldn't wait
          till tonight. I'm rash and
          impulsive -- it's a flaw.

                    FORD
          We all have flaws.

                    BUFFY
          So I'm constantly learning. I'm
          still fuzzy on exactly what yours is.
          I think it has to do with being a
          lying scumbag.

                    FORD
          Everybody lies.

                                              CONTINUED

> BUFFY
> But not everybody is a lying scumbag.
> There's a difference.

> FORD
> Yeah, I guess there is.

> BUFFY
> What do you want, Ford? What's this
> all about?

> FORD
> I really don't think you'd understand.

> BUFFY
> I don't need to understand. I just
> need to know.

> FORD
> I'm gonna be one of them.

> BUFFY
> One of them. You want to become a
> vampire.

> FORD
> I'm going to.

> BUFFY
> Vampires are kind of picky about who
> they change.
>   (realizes)
> So you were gonna offer them a trade.

> FORD
> I don't think I want to talk anymore.

She slams him up against the wall, hand to his throat.

> BUFFY
> Well, I still feel kind of chatty.
> You were gonna give them me. Tonight.

> FORD
> Yes.

> BUFFY
> What, lure me into the old building,
> leave me there for them?

> FORD
> Something like that.

*

CONTINUED

38 CONTINUED: (3)   38

                        BUFFY (cont'd)
            You had to know I'd figure it out,
            Ford.

                        FORD
                    (smiles)
            Actually, I was counting on it.

She steps back, wary. Her mind working.

                        BUFFY
            What's supposed to happen tonight?

                        FORD
            This is **so cool**! This is just like
            it played in my head. The part where
            you ask me what's supposed to happen.
            It's already happening.

She looks around. Dark spaces, weird people looking at her.
Sussing the nature of the trap, she steps back. She looks up:

39 ANGLE: THE DOOR   39

Diego swings it shut. We hear large locks THUD into place.
The handle on this side has been removed. A thick panel
welded shut over it.

Buffy races up the stairs. Pulls at the door. Nothing. She
turns back to Ford. He's halfway up, others grouped behind.

                        FORD
            Rigged it up special. Once it's
            closed, it can only be opened from
            the outside. As soon as the sun
            sets, they'll be coming.

                        BUFFY
            Ford, if these people are still
            around when they get here --

                        DIEGO
            We'll be changed. All of us.

                        CHANTARELLE
            We're going to ascend to a new level
            of consciousness. Become like them,
            like the Lonely Ones.

                        FORD
            This is the end, Buffy.

CONTINUED

39 CONTINUED: 39

    He smiles at her, amidst his flock.

                  FORD (cont'd)
    No one gets out of here alive.

                        BLACK OUT.

        END OF ACT THREE

ACT FOUR

40 INT. THE SUNSET CLUB - SECONDS LATER - AFTERNOON   40

Buffy races down the stairs, looks around for an alternate
exit. Ford is on her heels.

                    BUFFY
          There's got to be a way out of here.

                    FORD
          This is a bomb shelter, Buffy. I
          knew I wasn't gonna be able to
          overpower you. But this is three
          feet of solid concrete. Trust me
          when I saw we're here for the long
          haul.

                    BUFFY
          At least let these people out of here.

                    DIEGO
          No way! No fair!   We're a part of
          this, you promised.

                    FORD
          It doesn't matter. There's no key,
          there's no exit... let's all just sit
          back and relax.

Buffy slaps him in the face.

                    FORD (cont'd)
          You have an interesting way of
          relaxing.

                    BUFFY
          Do you have any idea what you've done?

                    FORD
          I do what I have to.

                    BUFFY
          What you **have** to?

                    CHANTARELLE
          Why are you fighting it? It's what
          we want.

                    DIEGO
          It's our chance for immortality.

                                        CONTINUED

40 CONTINUED: 40

                          CHANTARELLE
               This is a beautiful day! Can't you
               see that?

                          BUFFY
               What I can see is that right after
               the sun goes down Spike and his
               friends are gonna be pigging out at
               the all-you-can-eat moron bar!

                          DIEGO
               That's it. I think we should gag her.

                          BUFFY
                    (gives him the look)
               I think you should try.

                          DIEGO
               She's an unbeliever. She taints us.

                          BUFFY
               I'm trying to save you! You're
               playing in some serious traffic here,
               do you understand that? You're gonna
               DIE. The only hope you have of
               surviving is to get out of this pit
               right now and my God could you HAVE
               a dorkier outfit?

                          FORD
               Gotta back her up, D. You look like
               a big ninny.

A little ALARM goes off. Ford digs into his pocket, pulls
out a pager. Smiles.   *

                          FORD (cont'd)
               6:27. Sunset.

41 INT. THE FACTORY - 6:27 (NIGHT)   41

Spike sits at the head of the table, feet up. He holds an
antique pocket watch, the face dangling in front of his.
Reads it. Closes it.

                          SPIKE
               So. Who's hungry?

42   INT. SAME - SECONDS LATER - NIGHT   42

It's a sudden flurry of activity, as Vampires come downstairs
and out from the shadows, ready for the hunt. (There are
three besides Spike, Dru and Julia). They all head to the
door at which Drusilla waits.

                    SPIKE
          When we get there, everybody spread
          out. Two men on the door. First
          priority is the Slayer, everything
          else is fair game but let's remember
          to **share**, people.

He comes abreast of Dru.

                    SPIKE (cont'd)
          Sure you're up for this?

                    DRUSILLA
          I want a treat. I need a treat.

                    SPIKE
          And a special one you'll have.
          Lucius!

Spike holds up a set of keys, tosses them to a vampire.

                    SPIKE (cont'd)
          Bring the car 'round.

43   INT. THE SUNSET CLUB - NIGHT   43

Buffy is still intent on finding a way out. She ascends to
the metal bridge, eyes on the bricked-up windows. Ford
follows.

                    FORD
          Man, you never give up, do you?

                    BUFFY
          No, I don't.

                    FORD
          That's a good quality in a person.
          Too many people, they just lay back
          and take it. But us --

                    BUFFY
          Us? We have something in common now?

                    FORD
          More than you'd think.

                                        CONTINUED

                     BUFFY
Let me explain this to you. You're
what we call the bad guy.

                     FORD
I guess I am. Cool.

                     BUFFY
These people aren't gonna get
changed, are they? You, maybe, in
exchange for me, but the rest of
them -- they're just fodder.

                     FORD
Technically, yes. But I'm in. I
will become immortal.

                     BUFFY
I got a newsflash, braintrust.
That's not how it works. You die.
And a demon sets up shop in your old
house. It walks and talks and
remembers your life but it's not you.

                     FORD
It's better than nothing.

                     BUFFY
Your life is nothing?

He laughs a bit, bitterly.

                     BUFFY (cont'd)
Ford, these people don't deserve to
die.

                     FORD
Neither do I! But apparently nobody
took that into consideration, 'cause
I'm still dying.

This stops her.

                     FORD (cont'd)
I look good, don't I? Let me tell
you something. I got maybe six
months left and by then what they
bury won't even look like me. It'll
be bald and shriveled and it'll smell
bad. Not human. I'm not going out
that way.

CONTINUED

43 CONTINUED: (2)   43

Off her reaction.

                    FORD (cont'd)
          I'm sorry, Summers, did I screw up
          your righteous anger riff? Does the
          nest of tumors liquefying my brain
          kind of spoil the fun?

                    BUFFY
          I'm sorry. I had no idea... But
          this is still very wrong.

                    FORD
          Okay, well, you try vomiting for
          twenty four hours straight because
          the pain your head is so intense and
          then we'll discuss the concept of
          right and wrong.
                    (indicating the
                     others)
          These people are sheep. They want to
          be vampires 'cause they're lonely, or
          miserable, or bored. I don't have a
          choice.

                    BUFFY
          You have a choice. You don't have a
          good choice: what's behind door
          number three is pretty much a dead
          fish but you have a choice. You're
          opting for mass murderer here and
          nothing you say to me is gonna make
          that okay.

                    FORD
          You think I need to justify myself to
          you?

                    BUFFY
          I think this is part of your little
          fantasy drama. Isn't this just how
          you imagined it? You tell me how
          you've suffered and I feel sorry for
          you. Well I do feel sorry for you
          and if those vampires come in here
          and start feeding I'll kill you
          myself.

For a moment, Ford betrays an entirely genuine affection. He
almost smiles, and quietly says:

                                                    CONTINUED

43 CONTINUED: (3)   43

                         FORD
            You know what, Summers? I really did
            miss you.

There is a NOISE behind the iron door. Of people approaching.

                         BUFFY
            Ford, please. Help me stop this.

He just stares at her.

She heads around the balcony and down the stairs. A few have
gathered on them, the others clustered behind.

                         BUFFY (cont'd)
            Listen to me. This is not the
            mothership, okay? This is ugly death
            come to play. If we can barricade
            the door maybe we can hold them off
            and try to find another --

WHAM! Ford slams her in the back of the head with a crowbar.
Whatever emotion he was battling has left the building. His
face is cold.

Buffy drops to her knees as people scatter. She rises,
turns -- Ford hits her again and she goes over a couch.

44 ANGLE: CHANTARELLE   44

Looks at Ford in fear and confusion. She starts up the
stairs for the door.

45 ANGLE: THE DOOR -   45

swings open. Spike an his cronies step in. He comes face to
face with Chantarelle.

He's not quite what she expected.

He grabs her, snarls, bares his fangs. She goes white with
terror.

                         SPIKE
                    (to his men)
            Take them all. Save the Slayer for
            me!

His men charge down the steps and wade into the now panicking
throng. Spike buries his fangs in Chantarelle's neck.

46 ANGLE: BUFFY   46

As Ford comes around the couch for a third hit. She grabs
the bar, wrenches it free and slams Ford head first into a
pillar. He drops like a sack of unconscious person.

Buffy looks at the scene: Vamps chase or wrestle with various
True Believers. Buffy looks up to see:

47 ANGLE: DRUSILLA   47

Who has wandered in last, and stands on the balcony a ways
away from the busily feeding Spike.

Without hesitation Buffy runs - jumps onto the bannister,
thence to the balcony with impossible (and wire-gag-free)
strength. She lands by Drusilla and grabs her, whips out a
stake and places it at Dru's heart.

                    BUFFY
          Spike!

He stops. Fear blossoms on his face and he lets go of
Chantarelle, who can barely stand.

                    SPIKE
          Everybody **STOP!**

Everybody does.

                    BUFFY
          Good idea. Now they all walk out or
          your girlfriend fits in an ashtray.

                    DRUSILLA
          Spike...

                    SPIKE
          It's gonna be all right, baby.
                (to his men)
          Let them go.

The True Believers waste no time in going, Diego pushing his
way to the front. The last of them stops to help Chantarelle
out.

Buffy starts pushing Dru toward the door.

                    BUFFY
                (to Spike)
          Down the stairs. Do it now.

He doesn't.

                                                    CONTINUED

47 CONTINUED: 47

                              BUFFY (cont'd)
                    You think I'm joking? You think I'm
                    feeling jolly right now?

He does.

Buffy reaches the door. A moment. Then she hurls Drusilla
down at Spike. Spike catches Dru as a couple of Vampires
rush Buffy. She grabs the door and steps out, slamming it
shut behind her.

Spike races up to the door with his men, looks at it. Pauses.

                              SPIKE
                    Uh, where's the doorknob?

46 EXT. STREET - CONTINUOUS - NIGHT   48

Buffy steps out to find Xander, Angel and Willow there.
Angel is heading inside as Xander and Willow tend the
wounded. Angel stops upon seeing Buffy.

                              BUFFY
                    You guys got here just in time... to
                    be late.

                              ANGEL
                    Why didn't you tell us you were
                    coming here?

She just looks at him.

                              WILLOW
                    Are there vampires --

                              BUFFY
                    They're contained. They'll get out
                    eventually, though. We should clear
                    out. We can come back when they're
                    gone.

                              XANDER
                    Come back for what?

Buffy turns to look inside.

                              BUFFY
                    For the body.

49 INT. THE SUNSET CLUB - NIGHT   49

As Ford stands groggily up, looks around him.

CONTINUED

49   CONTINUED: 49

                         FORD
               What happened?

Spike turns, looking bloody-minded.

                         SPIKE
               We're stuck in the basement.

                         FORD
               Buffy?

                         SPIKE
               She's **not** stuck in the basement.

                         FORD
               Hey, well, I delivered. I handed her
               to you.

                         SPIKE
               Yes, I suppose you did.

                         FORD
               So what about my reward?

Spike stares at him.

50   INT. THE SUNSET CLUB - AFTERNOON   50

We can actually see light streaming in through the door --
which is ripped mostly off its hinges. Buffy enters, walks
slowly down the stairs.

The body is on the floor. She stands over it.

51   EXT. GRAVEYARD - SUNSET   51

The last rays of the sun are glancing off the trees as Buffy
stands at Ford's grave, Giles beside her.   *

                         BUFFY
               I don't know what I'm supposed to say.

                         GILES
               You needn't say anything.

                         BUFFY
               It'd be simpler if I could just hate
               him. I think he wanted me to. I
               think it made it easier for him. Be
               the bad guy. The villain of the
               piece. But really, he was scared.

                                                   CONTINUED

                         GILES
          I suppose he was.

                         BUFFY
          You know, it's just, like, nothing's
          simple. I'm always trying to work it
          out. Who to hate, or love... who to
          trust... It's like the more I know,
          the more confused I get.

                         GILES
          I believe that's called growing up.

                         BUFFY
                (little voice)
          I'd like to stop, then. Okay?

                         GILES
          I know the feeling.

                         BUFFY
          Well, does it ever get easy?

Ford BURSTS from the grave, a snarling VAMPIRE, and lunges at
Buffy -- who plants a stake firmly in his chest. She doesn't
even look as he explodes into dust.

                         GILES
          You mean life?

                         BUFFY
          Yeah. Does it get easy?

                         GILES
          What do you want me to say?

She thinks about it a moment.

                         BUFFY
          Lie to me.

                         GILES
          Yes. It's terribly simple.

As they start out of the graveyard:

                         GILES (cont'd)
          The good-guys are stalwart and true.
          The bad-guys are easily distinguished
          by their pointy horns or black hats
          and we always defeat them and save
          the day. Nobody ever dies...
                (more)

51 CONTINUED: (2)   51

                    GILES (cont'd)
          and everyone lives happily ever after.

                                        BLACK OUT.

                    BUFFY (O.S.)
                 (with weary affection)
          Liar.

                    END OF SHOW

BUFFY THE VAMPIRE SLAYER

"The Dark Age"

Written By

Dean Batali
&
Rob DesHotel

Directed By

Bruce Seth Green

SHOOTING SCRIPT

September 23, 1997 (WHITE)
September 24, 1997 (BLUE)
September 25, 1997 (PINK)
September 30, 1997 (YELLOW)
October 2, 1997 (GREEN)

BUFFY THE VAMPIRE SLAYER

"The Dark Age"

CAST LIST

BUFFY SUMMERS........................... Sarah Michelle Gellar
XANDER HARRIS........................... Nicholas Brendon
RUPERT GILES........................... Anthony S. Head
WILLOW ROSENBERG....................... Alyson Hannigan
CORDELIA CHASE......................... Charisma Carpenter
ANGEL................................. David Boreanaz

JENNY CALENDAR........................ Robia La Morte
ETHAN RAYNE........................... Robin Sachs
PHILIP................................ Stuart McLean
*DEIRDRE (CORPSE WOMAN)................ Wendy Way
CUSTODIAN............................. Michael Earl Reid
CREEPY CULT GUY.......................
WINSLOW...............................*Carlease Burke
MORGUE ATTENDANT...................... Tony Sears
VAMP DRIVER...........................*Chris O'Hara
MAN................................... John Bellucci

BUFFY THE VAMPIRE SLAYER

"The Dark Age"

<u>SET LIST</u>

<u>INTERIORS</u>

SUNNYDALE HIGH SCHOOL
    HALL
    LIBRARY
        GILES' OFFICE
    *LOUNGE
    *COMPUTER LAB

GILES' APARTMENT
    *HALL OUTSIDE

GROOVY 70's PAD

MORGUE

ETHAN'S COSTUME SHOP

<u>EXTERIORS</u>

SUNNYDALE HIGH SCHOOL
    WALKWAY

HOSPITAL
    *LOADING DOCK

GILES' APARTMENT

MORGUE (STOCK)

STREET

BUFFY THE VAMPIRE SLAYER

"The Dark Age"

TEASER

1 EXT. SUNNYDALE HIGH - NIGHT   1

Deserted. A MAN (PHILIP HENRY, 40-ish) walks towards us,
grows into a TIGHT, C.U. He's desperate, sheen of sweat on
his face. Startled by:

                    CUSTODIAN (O.S.)
               Can I help you?

Philip turns, sees the CUSTODIAN about to empty some trash in
a dumpster, eyeing him suspiciously. Philip has a BRITISH
ACCENT.

                    PHILIP
               Rupert Giles. I need to see him...

                    CUSTODIAN
               Mr. Giles, he's our librarian. Next
               building over, first door on your
               left.

Philip moves off, picking up the pace, disappearing around a
corner.

                    CUSTODIAN (cont'd)
               You're welcome.

2 EXT. NEXT BUILDING OVER - NIGHT - CONTINUOUS   2

Philip rounds the corner. Sees, several yards away, the door
marked CLASSROOM BUILDING/LIBRARY. He hears a NOISE and
turns, his heart pounding. Peers into the darkness. Nothing.
He moves towards the door.

We HEAR a sticky, sickening sound, something definitely
moving now in the darkness. Philip looks again. And this
time IT MOVES out of the shadows: a SILHOUETTE with GLOWING
EYES.

                    PHILIP
               Oh God...

Philip steps back, nearly trips on the steps outside the
building (or something else conveniently placed in his path.)

The figure moves unrelentingly closer. It's a living,
walking CORPSE. A woman. Skin long dead and a sickly shade
of blue. She was forty when she died.

                                                      CONTINUED

2 CONTINUED: 2

And Philip's knees nearly buckle as he recognizes:

                    PHILIP (cont'd)
          ...Deirdre?   *

Deirdre smiles. It's not a pleasant smile, full of BLACK,   *
ROTTED TEETH and all. The woman advances. Philip finds his
legs and runs. Gets to the door.

                    PHILIP (cont'd)
          God, no! Help!

He fumbles with door -- is it locked? -- no, he gets it open,
but not very far when DEIRDRE's grisly hand slams it shut.   *

                    PHILIP (cont'd)
          Help me...!

3 INT. LIBRARY - NIGHT - SAME TIME   3

Loud, thumping DANCE MUSIC BLARES from a portable stereo,
drowning out the outside world, as BUFFY goes through an
intense STEP-AEROBICS routine. Nearby, GILES attempts to
read a book-- both hands plastered over his ears. He brings
one hand down to take a sip of tea.

                    GILES
              (shouts above music)
          Must we have such noise during your
          calisthenics?

                    BUFFY
          It's not noise, it's music.

                    GILES
          I know music. Music has notes. This
          is noise.

                    BUFFY
          I'm aerobicizing. I must have the
          beat.

                    GILES
          Wonderful. You work on your muscle
          tone while my brains dribble out my
          ears.

4 EXT. SUNNYDALE HIGH - NIGHT - SAME TIME   4

                    PHILIP
          Somebody, please!

CONTINUED

4 CONTINUED: 4

Corpse Woman glides her arm around Philip's neck from behind: almost a lover's caress -- until it tightens around his neck, squeezing the life out of him. Her eyes GLOW brighter -- Philip's final scream is cut short -- we hear the unmistakable CRACK of Philip's neck being BROKEN.

5 INT. LIBRARY - NIGHT - SAME TIME   5

The song ends, Buffy finishing her exercise routine.

                         GILES
              Ah. Very good. The rest is silence.

                                                    CUT TO:

6 EXT. SUNNYDALE HIGH - NIGHT - SAME TIME   6

Philip lies there, dead. His eyes stare blankly.

PULL BACK to see Corpse Woman towering over him. Her eyes stop glowing. Her body wavers for a moment, then her knees give out as she FALLS TO THE GROUND...

...and her body DISINTEGRATES, incredibly, into a pool of liquid ooze. And the liquid rolls downhill, a little of it washing the fingers of Philip's dead hand.

                                           BLACK OUT.

                    END OF TEASER

ACT ONE

7   INT. GROOVY 70's PAD - NIGHT   7

FLAMES FILL THE SCREEN

and deafening seventies PUNK MUSIC plays as various IMAGES
overlap in a STYLIZED way: JERKY CAMERA MOVEMENTS, QUICK
ZOOMS and RAPID CUTS.

(PRODUCTION NOTE: We should do all these in one location if
possible. Since it's a dream I see no reason not to do it
against blacks hung in, say, the Bronze.)

1) CLOSE-UP of a NEEDLE administering an ominous, SYMBOLIC-
LOOKING TATTOO on someone's arm. We'll see this tattoo again.

2) A CREEPY CULT GUY -- sort of a cross between Jim Morrison
and Charles Manson -- dressed in seventies' style clothes
with reflecting sunglasses on, smiles at us.

                    CREEPY CULT GUY
                   (English accent)
            Time to go to sleep.

3) The flames BURN BRIGHTER

4) Six hands join in the center of a circle. Painted on the
floor is the same mark as the tattoo.

5) Creepy Cult Guy again, only now he is POSSESSED. His face
thrashes back and forth, and through the BLUR we catch
glimpses of a DEMON: blue skin, rotted and pocked flesh,
ridges on his forehead.

8   INT. GILES' APARTMENT - MORNING   8

Giles bolts awake, out of his dream. He's sweating,
breathing hard. He wipes his hand across his face, looks at
his clock: 6:05 AM.

He THROWS the covers off and they FILL THE SCREEN. When they
fall, we have:

                                           CUT TO:

9   EXT. SUNNYDALE HIGH - THAT MORNING   9

Only a few STUDENTS are there as BUFFY sits with WILLOW

                                                        CONTINUED

9 CONTINUED: 9

> BUFFY
> I'm on a beach. Not an American
> beach -- one of those island beaches
> where the water is way too blue.
> It's just before sunset, I'm lying on
> a towel and Gavin Rossdale is
> massaging my feet.

> WILLOW
> That's good. Uh, I'm in Florence,
> Italy. I've rented a scooter which
> is parked outside. I'm in a little
> restaurant having ziti and there's no
> more tables to they have to seat this
> guy with me and it's John Cusack.

> BUFFY
> Very impressive. An eye for detail.

> WILLOW
>   (excited)
> 'Cause, with the ziti.

XANDER joins them.

> XANDER
> What are you guys up to?

> BUFFY
> Just having a quick game of "Anywhere
> But Here."

> XANDER
> Amy Yip at the waterslide park.

> WILLOW
> You never come up with anything new.

They start towards the door.

> XANDER
> I'm not fickle like you two, okay?
> I'm constant in my affections. Amy
> Yip at the waterslide park.

They see Giles lecturing a student by the door.

> WILLOW
> You think Giles ever played "Anywhere
> But Here" in school?

                                                    CONTINUED

> XANDER
> Giles lived for school. He's still
> bitter there were only twelve grades.

> BUFFY
> He probably sat in math class
> thinking, "There should be more math!
> This could be mathier."

> WILLOW
> You don't think he ever got restless
> when he was little?

> BUFFY
> Are you kidding? His diapers were
> tweed.

They reach Giles, who falls in step with Buffy.

> GILES
> Ah. There you are.

> BUFFY
> Morning. Say, is that tweed?

> GILES
> What? Oh. Well, yes. Now, tonight   *
> is a very important --   *

> BUFFY
>   (still looking at his   *
>   outfit)   *
> You know, Giles, I realize the Henry   *
> Higgins bit may have been the mod   *
> look for your generation, but a lot   *
> has happened since then. Like the   *
> 20th Century, for example.   *

> GILES
> As an educator, it behooves me to set   *
> myself apart from you students by my   *
> mode of dress and demeanor.   *

> BUFFY
> Is it stuffy in here, or is it just   *
> you?   *

> GILES
> Laugh all you want, but the problem   *
> with this culture is its disregard   *
> for decorum, which I believe has led   *
> to the current pursuit of feel-good   *
> nihilism.   *

CONTINUED

9 CONTINUED: (3)   9

                    XANDER
          What have I been saying for years?

                    WILLOW
          That you'll die a virgin? Oh. The
          nihilism thing. Sorry. Missed the
          funny there.

     They enter the building.

10 INT. SCHOOL HALL - DAY   10   *

                                              CONTINUED

10 CONTINUED: 10

                         BUFFY
          So, what's on tap tonight that's so
          important? Uprising? Prophesized
          ritual? Preordained death-fest?

                         XANDER
          Ah, the old standards.

                         GILES
          A transport vehicle is delivering a
          supply of blood to the hospital.

                         BUFFY
          Aha. Vampire meals-on-wheels.

                         GILES
          Well, hopefully not. We should meet
          in front of the hospital at 8:30
          sharp. I'll bring the weaponry.

                         BUFFY
          And I'll bring the party mix.

                         GILES
                    (stern look)
          Just don't be late.

                         BUFFY
          Giles, have I ever let you down?

                         GILES
          Do you want me to answer that, or
          shall I just glare?

     MS. CALENDAR approaches. Giles brightens when he sees her.

                                                    CONTINUED

10 CONTINUED: (2)   10

                    JENNY
               (smiling)
          Morning, England.

                    GILES
          Hello, Ms... Jenny.

                    WILLOW
               (aside, to Xander)
          Feel the passion.

                    JENNY
          Willow--

                    WILLOW
               (coughs)
          Coughing, not speaking.

                    JENNY
          --we're still on for tomorrow?

Willow nods.

                    XANDER
          What's tomorrow?

                    JENNY
          I'm reviewing some computer basics
          with a couple of students who have
          fallen behind. Willow's helping for
          extra credit.

                    XANDER
          Hah! Those poor schlubs. Having to
          give up their Saturday--

                    JENNY
          Nine a.m. okay with you, Xander?

Xander's face falls.

                    BUFFY
               (to Xander)
          You've got a bit of schlub on your
          shoe, there.

                    JENNY
          Cordelia is going to meet us.

                    XANDER
          Hey, gang, did you hear that? A bonus
          day of class, plus Cordelia!
               (more)

                                              CONTINUED

10 CONTINUED: (3)   10

                         XANDER (cont'd)
               A little rectal surgery and it would
               be the <u>best</u> <u>day</u> <u>ever</u>!

                         JENNY
                    (to Giles)
               Walk me to class?

                         GILES
               Pleasure.

                         JENNY
               Nice coat.

                         GILES
                    (for Buffy's benefit)
               Tweed, you know.

A BELL RINGS. Calendar and Giles head down the hall which
begins to empty as students enter classrooms. Buffy smiles
after them.

                         BUFFY
               Look at them.

                         XANDER
               A twosome of cuteness.

                         WILLOW
               Can't you just imagine them getting
               together?

The three WATCH THEM FONDLY for a beat. Then, as the image
sinks in: they SHUDDER.

11 INT. HALLWAY - A MOMENT LATER - DAY   11

The hallway is nearly empty as Giles and Calendar walk.

                         JENNY
               Oh! Thank you so much for loaning me
               the Forrester book. It's wonderful.

                         GILES
               I'm glad you enjoyed it.

                         JENNY
               It was so romantic, so evocative.

                         GILES
               That edition was my father's. I must
               have read it 20 times.

                                                    CONTINUED

11 CONTINUED: 11

                         JENNY
          You know how you have to dog-ear your
          favorite pages so you can go back to
          them?

                         GILES
                    (alarmed)
          You have to what?

                         JENNY
          Well, I practically folded back every
          page. So I underlined the passages
          I really wanted to discuss.

                         GILES
                    (queasy)
          Underlined?

                         JENNY
          But then I spilled coffee on it and
          I couldn't even read it.

                         GILES
          Coffee. On the first edition.

                         JENNY
                    (smiles)
          I'm lying, Rupert. The book's fine.
          I just love to see you squirm.

                         GILES
          Oh. Well, I trust I gave good squirm.

                         JENNY
          Did anyone ever tell you you're kind
          of a fuddy duddy?

                         GILES
          Nobody ever seems to tell me anything
          else.

She moves closer to him.

                         JENNY
          Did anyone ever tell you you're kind
          of a sexy fuddy duddy?

                         GILES
          That part usually gets left out. I
          can't imagine why.

                         JENNY
          This weekend --

                                                          CONTINUED

11 CONTINUED: (2)   11

                         GILES
               Would you like to go out?

                         JENNY
               I think I'd like to stay in.

The implications of this are not lost on Giles. They lean in
for a kiss -- their lips meet -- they get off about a
second's worth before a door opens and kids are charging
through them. They separate, her smiling ruefully, him
nervously trying to maintain decorum.

                         GILES
               This Saturday night, then?

                         JENNY
               Saturday night. I'll see if I can
               make you squirm.

                         GILES
               Oh! Yes. I'm ... yes. Put me down
               for squirminess.
                         (beat)
               A suave person would have just shut
               up and walked away right then,
               wouldn't he?

                         JENNY
                         (smiles)
               Possibly.

                         GILES
               Well, why don't I try now.

With a nod, he goes. She watches him affectionately. Heads
in the other direction.

12 INT. LIBRARY - CONTINUOUS - DAY   12

Giles comes in and stops short. Two UNIFORMED COPS and A
POLICE WOMAN stand there. Looking very official and a little
menacing.

                         WINSLOW
               Rupert Giles?

                         GILES
               Yes?

                                                        CONTINUED

12 CONTINUED: 12

                    WINSLOW
              (flashes her badge)
     Detective Winslow. You're going to
     have to come with me.

                    GILES
     Why?

                    WINSLOW
     There was a homicide on campus last
     night. The victim had no
     identification. But he was carrying
     this slip of paper with your name and
     address on it.

Winslow shows Giles the slip of paper (in a tagged evidence
baggy.) Giles peers at it through the plastic.

CORDELIA bursts through the library door.

                    GILES
     My name?

                    CORDELIA
     Well, evil just compounds evil,
     doesn't it. First I'm sentenced to
     a computer tutorial on Saturday, now
     I have to read some computer book.
     They have books about computers?
     Isn't that the point of computers, to
     replace books?

                    GILES
     Cordelia, I'm a little busy just
     now...

He indicates the cops. She sees them as if for the first
time, says to one of the uniforms:

                    CORDELIA
     Oh, great. Can you help me with a
     ticket? It's totally bogus, a one
     way street, I was going one way --

                    GILES
     Cordelia!

                    CORDELIA
     What? Why does everybodt always yell
     my name? I'm not deaf. And I can
     take a hint.

Long beat.

                                        CONTINUED

12 CONTINUED: (2)   12

                    CORDELIA (cont'd)
          What's the hint?

                    GILES
          To come back later.

                    CORDELIA
          Yeah, when you've visited decaf-land.

She leaves. Giles turns back to the Police Woman.

                    GILES
          Where is it you want me to go?

                                        SMASH CUT:

13 INT. MORGUE - LATER THAT DAY - A SHEETED BODY   13

Rolls out in a drawer. A MORGUE ATTENDANT eyes Giles.
Detective Winslow stands nearby.

                    MORGUE ATTENDANT
          Have you had breakfast?

                    GILES
          No.

                    MORGUE ATTENDANT
          That was probably a good idea.

The Morgue Attendant pulls the sheet off of the body,   *
revealing Philip, the man killed in the Teaser.

A look of RECOGNITION crosses Giles' face and he reacts,
visibly upset.

                    WINSLOW
          Do you know him?

Giles stares hard, then:

                    GILES
          Yes. I mean, I did. His name is
          Philip Henry. He was a friend of
          mine in London. I haven't spoken to
          him in twenty years.

                    WINSLOW
          Can you think of any reason he might
          have wanted to contact you?

                                        CONTINUED

13 CONTINUED: 13

Giles pauses for a bit, fixated on something.

                    GILES
          No...

REVEAL Giles is staring at a TATTOO on Philip's forearm (the same tattoo Giles saw in his dream).

                    WINSLOW
          Do you know what that is? The tattoo?

Giles looks at the tattoo, at the police woman.

                    GILES
          No. No, I don't.

                                        DISSOLVE TO:

14 EXT. HOSPITAL LOADING DOCK - NIGHT   14

Buffy waits. Checks her watch. INSERT WATCH: it reads 9:03. Buffy looks around, concerned: no Giles.

                    BUFFY
          "Don't be late."   Sheesh.

Moves to a pay phone, drops in a quarter, dials. Gets a busy signal.

                    BUFFY (cont'd)
          Giles, why is your phone busy when
          you're supposed to be here?

She punches O.

                    BUFFY (cont'd)
          Operator, can you check a line for
          me...

Then headlights wash across her face.

                    BUFFY (cont'd)
          Never mind. Sorry.

She hangs up, moves back into the shadows, watching:

BUFFY'S POV - A STATION WAGON OR VAN

"Medical Transport" stencilled on the side. Pulls to a stop at the loading dock.

                                                    CONTINUED

14 CONTINUED: 14

BUFFY WATCHES

As the DRIVER gets out, moves to a couple of INTERNS (two
guys in hospital scrubs, hospital tags on the shirt pocktes,
one has a stethoscope around his neck). One of the INTERNS
signs a clipboard the Driver holds for him, the other hefts
a large ice chest out of the van.

The Driver gets in his car and drives away. Buffy watches
the YOUNG INTERNS head for the hospital back door.

                    BUFFY (cont'd)
          All's well that ends with cute E.R.
          doctors I always say.

She turns and starts away. The stops.

                    BUFFY (cont'd)
          Since when do doctors take deliveries?

Buffy sees the interns move past the back door and pick up
their pace, heading down the side of the building. She moves
into action, vaulting off the wall or over something
interesting in the set and closing the gap.

ANGLE - SIDE OF BUILDING

One of the "interns" rips off his stethoscope and pulls a
blood bag out of the ice chest the other one carries.
They're heading towards a MUSCLE CAR parked nearby. The
driver of that car steps out. He is a vampire.

                    VAMP DRIVER
          Hey, no sampling the product.

The "intern" (let's call him vamp 1 from now on since now
he's a vamp) ignores the driver, bites into the bag. The
other intern, (call him vamp 2) growls at him.

Then a shadowy figure leaps on vamp 1 from behind.

And now Buffy runs, pulling out a stake, leaping into the
air, coming down on the shadowy figure's back, about to sink
the stake, when he turns and she recognizes:

                    BUFFY
          Angel!

She holds up with the stake just in time.

                    ANGEL
          Buffy! Look out!

                                                      CONTINUED

14 CONTINUED: (2)   14

Vamp-driver RAMS shoulder-first into Buffy, taking her to the
ground. He turns on Angel who hits him real darn hard.

Vamp 1 dives for Buffy, gets a stake. Vamp 2 comes at Angel
who uses Vamp 2's velocity to whip him around and send him
towards Buffy.

                    ANGEL (cont'd)
          Incoming!

Buffy stakes him, too. A ROARING ENGINE causes them to look
over at the muscle car as vamp-driver roars away.

                    BUFFY
          How did you know about this?

                    ANGEL
          It's delivery day. Everybody knows
          about this.
                    (re: ice chest of
                     blood bags)
          They only ruined one bag.

                    BUFFY
          Can you make sure the hospital gets
          the rest?
                    (he nods)
          I'm worried about Giles. He was
          supposed to meet me here.

                    ANGEL
          Maybe he's late.

                    BUFFY
          Giles? Who counts tardiness as the
          eighth deadly sin?

                    ANGEL
          Right. Go.

She does.

                                                    CUT TO:

15 EXT. GILES' APARTMENT - NIGHT - STOCK   15

Establishing.

16 INT. HALL OUTSIDE GILES' APARTMENT - NIGHT   16

Buffy, fresh from the fight, moves down the hall, listens at
the door for a moment. Hears Giles' muffled voice.

                    GILES (O.S.)
          Are you certain she didn't leave a
          forwarding number? I've been on the
          phone for hours, this is a matter of
          life and --

Buffy knocks. A couple of beats, then Giles opens the door
a CRACK, stares out at Buffy. He's unshaven, in
shirtsleeves, looking a good deal more rumpled than we've
ever seen him.

                    GILES
          Buffy. It's late, are you all right?

                    BUFFY
          I was going to ask you the same thing.

                    GILES
          Yes, fine. I'm afraid I'm rather
          busy. I'll see you Monday at
          school --

He tries to shut the door. She stops it.

                    BUFFY
          Giles, did you forget about the
          hospital? Vampires? Bags of blood
          in handy carry out packets?

                    GILES
          Oh. Are you all right? Were you
          hurt?

                    BUFFY
          No. I mean, my feelings a little.
          What's wrong?

                    GILES
          Nothing. Nothing's wrong, I'm in the
          middle of an extremely important
          matter and I'm sorry but I'm just
          going to have to say good night now.

And he forces the door closed. She hears him LOCK it from
inside. Then footsteps. Then his MUFFLED VOICE again on the
phone.

                    GILES (OS)
          Are you still there? Yes, any
          number, a relative, anything...

                                              CONTINUED

16   CONTINUED: 16

      Buffy stares at the door for a beat. Then turns and goes.
      Hold the door.

17   INT. GILES' APARTMENT - NIGHT   17

      The lights are dimmed, the shades drawn. Giles is tense,
      finishes dialing a number on the phone. He HEARS a ring and
      then an answer.

                         GILES
                    (into phone)
                I'm sorry to disturb you, I realize
                it's five in the morning there but
                I'm trying to reach Dierdre Page. My
                name is Rupert Giles, she knows me,
                it's very important...

      Giles listens for a beat, his face falling.

                         GILES (cont'd)
                I'm terribly sorry, I didn't know..
                when did she pass away? Oh dear, that
                recently. We were friends when we
                were young... my condolences.

      Giles hangs up. Worst fears realized. He slumps down in a
      chair. There's a bottle and a glass. He drinks something
      strong from the glass, then turns his attention to:

      A LIST - with a few names on it.

      The first two are CROSSED OUT: Thomas Sutcliffe, Philip
      Henry. Giles crosses a line through the third: Deirdre Page.   *

      Then he looks lower on the list and we see the two names
      left: Ethan Rayne and Rupert Giles.

18   OMITTED   18

      Giles, distraught, moves to a mirror with a pitcher of water
      and a bowl in front of it. He rolls up his sleeves. That's
      when we see:

      THE TATTOO on his arm, identical to the one on Philip's arm.

      Giles fills his hands with cold water and splashes it on his
      face. He stares at himself in the mirror.

                                                    CONTINUED

17 CONTINUED: 17

> GILES
> So... you're back.

CUT TO:

19 EXT. MORGUE - NIGHT - STOCK 19

Establishing. Quiet. Dark.

DISSOLVE TO:

20 INT. MORGUE - SAME TIME - NIGHT 20

It's late at night, no one is around. The CAMERA MOVES towards the drawers on the wall and centers on one.

DISSOLVE TO:

INSIDE THE DRAWER

Looking down on Philip, who lies there. Still dead. Then a hand pulls the sheet back, a hand that can only belong to Philip. His eyes open. And begin to GLOW.

BLACK OUT.

END OF ACT ONE

ACT TWO

21 INT. MORGUE - NIGHT   21

The morgue attendant carries a clipboard as he heads to the
wall of drawers. He OPENS a drawer, looks at a temperature
gauge, jots something on the clipboard, and closes the drawer.

He goes to another drawer and does the same.

He moves to a third drawer, opens it, and REACTS, startled.

TILT DOWN to REVEAL the drawer is empty.

TILT BACK UP and REVEAL PHILIP, standing behind the attendant
in a very un-dead way. Philip is shirtless and, presumably,
corpse-naked. He looks like shit, being dead and all.

Philip THROWS A SHEET over the attendant's head and LIFTS him
into the air. As the attendant STRUGGLES beneath the sheet,
Philip stuffs him into the drawer and closes it. It CLICKS
SHUT, locking the attendant in.

Philip SHAMBLES OUT. We hear the MUFFLED SCREAMS of the
attendant as he helplessly POUNDS on the inside of the drawer.

                                          DISSOLVE TO:

22 EXT. SUNNYDALE HIGH - DAY - STOCK   22

The high school should be completely empty. Hoping we have
this in stock.

                    CORDELIA (O.S.)
              This is not right.

23 INT. SUNNYDALE HIGH (HALL) - DAY   23

Calendar, Willow, Xander and Cordelia move down the hall.

                    CORDELIA
              School on a Saturday? That throws
              off my internal clock.

                    XANDER
              When are we going to have to use
              computers in real life, anyway?

                    JENNY
              Let's see, there's home, school,
              work, games--

                                                    CONTINUED

23 CONTINUED: 23

                         XANDER
              Computers are on the way out. I
              think paper is about to make a big
              comeback.

                         WILLOW
              And the abacus.

                         XANDER
              Yeah. You don't see enough abaci.

Jenny unlocks the classroom door (the room across from the
library in fact) and they enter. Set up as a computer lab.

A24 INT. COMPUTER LAB - CONTINUOUS - DAY   A24

                         JENNY
              All right, the first thing we want to
              do is...
                    (sees)
              ...Buffy.

                         XANDER
              Huh? Did I fall asleep already?

He turns, sees Buffy in the door.

                         WILLOW
              Ahhh. You miss your friends.

                         XANDER
              Sit here, Buffs. De-militarize the
              zone between me and Cordelia.

                         CORDELIA
              And de-lice him while you're at it.

                         BUFFY
                    (to Jenny)
              Actually I wanted to talk to you for
              a second.

                         JENNY
              Is something wrong?

                         XANDER
              Is it some crisis that requires
              instant action -- very far from here?

                         BUFFY
              I'm not sure...

                                                        CONTINUED

                    XANDER
          <u>Think</u>, dammit! Buffy, don't make me
          beg.

                    BUFFY
          Well, it's Giles.

                    XANDER
          A loved one, good...

                    WILLOW
          He's all right, isn't he?

                    BUFFY
          I don't know. He didn't show up last
          night when he was supposed to, and
          then I went by his place and he was
          acting... well, very Anti-Giles.

                    WILLOW
          You went by his place? He has a
          place?
                    (off their looks)
          Of course he has a... I just never
          think of him living anywhere outside
          the library. So there was weirdness?

                    BUFFY
          He wouldn't let me in. He looked
          terrible. And I think he might have
          been... uh, I think he was drinking.

                    JENNY
          He was home alone drinking?

                    WILLOW
          But... <u>tea</u>, right?

                    BUFFY
          It wasn't tea, Will.

                    XANDER
          Yup. I knew this would happen.
          Nobody can be wound as straight and
          narrow as Giles without a dark side
          erupting. My Uncle Roary was the
          stodgiest taxidermist you ever met --
          by day -- by night it was booze and
          whores and fur flying... were there
          any whores?

                    WILLOW
          <u>Xander.</u>

                                              CONTINUED

A24 CONTINUED: (2)   A24

                        BUFFY
             He was alone.

                        XANDER
             Give it time.

                        BUFFY
             None of you have noticed anything
             different about him lately?

                        WILLOW
             No.

                        JENNY
             Not really.

                        BUFFY
             Haven't seen anything weird?

                        XANDER
             No.

                        CORDELIA
             He was perfectly normal yesterday
             when I saw him talking to the police.

     They all look at her.

                        BUFFY
             And you waited until now to tell us
             because...?

                        CORDELIA
             I didn't think it was important.

                        XANDER
             We understand. It wasn't about you.

                        JENNY
             What were the police talking to him
             about?

                        CORDELIA
             Don't tell me, I know this one...
             something about a... homicide.

                        BUFFY
             I'm calling him right now.

     Buffy exits.

24   INT. SCHOOL HALL - DAY   24

   We TRACK with her across the hall and into:

25   INT. LIBRARY - AND GILES' OFFICE - DAY   25

   She heads for GILES' OFFICE, is half inside (where we see the
   phone on his desk) when she hears a NOISE. She looks up.
   ANOTHER NOISE, coming from the stacks. She heads up the
   stairs and into:

26   INT. LIBRARY - THE STACKS - DAY   26

   Dark and eerie in here. Buffy MOVES in and out of the
   shadows and peers down one row. Something moves behind her,
   she turns, nothing there.

   She pins herself against a bookcase, MOVES to the end of the
   shelves, and checks another row. Again, nothing. She turns
   and looks through a rack.

   BUFFY'S POV: SOMEONE STARES BACK AT HER from the other side.

   Buffy jumps back, startled, then realizes the bookcase is
   COMING DOWN on her. She ROLLS out of the way before it
   CRASHES DOWN and sees the suspect SCRAMBLE AWAY.

   Buffy LEAPS over the downed bookcase and grabs him, spins him
   around. It's ETHAN RAYNE. Buffy doesn't immediately
   recognize him. Then --   *

                                                                  *

                  BUFFY
         I know you, you ran that costume shop.

                  ETHAN
         I'm pleased you remember.
                  BUFFY
         You sold me that dress for Halloween
         and nearly got us all killed.

                  ETHAN
         But you looked great.

                                          CONTINUED

26 CONTINUED: 26

       Buffy sends a RIGHT HOOK into his jaw. Ethan works his mouth
       back and forth.

                          ETHAN (cont'd)
                 So now we're even?

                          BUFFY
                 I'll let you know when we're even.
                      (then)
                 I'm going to ask you once again and
                 then I'm pretty much going straight
                 to the pummeling: what are you doing
                 here?

                          ETHAN
                 Snooping around.

                          BUFFY
                 Honesty. Nice touch.

                          ETHAN
                 It's one of my virtues.
                      (then)
                 Not really.

                          BUFFY
                 I got a great idea...

       Buffy grabs him.   *

27 OMITTED   27   *

                                                                  *

                          BUFFY (cont'd)
                 ...why don't I just call the police
                 and have you arrested for breaking
                 and entering and get back to my fun
                 Saturday.

                          ETHAN
                 Yes the police. They'll have so many
                 questions -- they'll really need
                 Rupert to answer them all.

                          BUFFY
                 You know Giles?

                          ETHAN
                 We go back. Way back. You wouldn't
                 happen to know where he is, would you?

                                                          CONTINUED

26 CONTINUED: (2)   26

      Off Ethan's look.

                                              CUT TO:

28 MORE MONTAGE - INT. BRONZE - NIGHTISH   28

      (PRODUCTION NOTE: NUMBERS 3 and 4 ARE SHOT ON THEIR
      RESPECTIVE LOCATIONS) Rapid, choppy images again, with the
      same LOUD MUSIC.

      1) FLAMES, as in the first dream.

      2) The possessed CREEPY CULT GUY, his demon visage engulfed
      in the flames, screaming in agony.

                        CREEPY CULT GUY
                  You're marked. I'll kill you for
                  this! I'll kill you all!

      3) CORPSE WOMAN (from the Teaser) stepping out of the shadows.

      4) PHILIP's corpse in the drawer. His eyes open and GLOW.

      5) A pane of glass as it SHATTRERS revealing a PHONE which
      is, incongruously, RINGING.

29 INT. GILES' APARTMENT - DAY   29

      Giles BOLTS AWAKE as the phone continues to RING. Dressed in
      last night's clothes, he was slumped at the table, the bottle
      pretty well empty now. he looks like shit.

                        GILES
                  Hello?

                                              INTERCUT:

30 BUFFY - INT. LIBRARY - DAY   30   *

      Buffy has the phone in one hand, Ethan's collar in the other.
      Ethan's shirt sleeve is rolled up, revealing the tattoo we've
      been seeing.

                        BUFFY
                  Giles, it's me.

                        GILES
                  Buffy. Unless this is an emergency,
                  I'll see you in school on Monday --

                        BUFFY
                  What's the Mark of Eyghon?

                                              CONTINUED

30   CONTINUED: 30

     Giles turns ashen on the other end.

                         BUFFY (cont'd)
                    Giles?

                         ETHAN
                    Cat got his tongue?

                         BUFFY
                    I'm in your office with someone who
                    claims to be an old friend of yours:
                    Ethan Rayne.

                         GILES
                    He's there with you?

     Giles glances down at his list and ETHAN'S NAME on it.

                         GILES (cont'd)
                    Buffy, listen to me. You're in great
                    danger with Ethan there. I want you
                    to put down the phone and get out of
                    the library as quickly as possible.

                         BUFFY
                    I'm not going anywhere until you
                    start giving me some answers --

     Philip CRASHES through a window in Giles' office. He is
     dressed in the clothes in which he was killed.

     Glass SHATTERS and FLIES. Philip comes for him. Ethan puts
     Buffy between himself and Philip.

31   INT. GILES' APARTMENT - SAME TIME - DAY   31

     Giles yells into the phone:

                         GILES
                    Buffy!

     He listens for half a beat to the sounds of destruction, then
     drops the phone and runs out of frame.

32   INT. LIBRARY - DAY   32   *

     Buffy roundhouse kicks (or punches) Philip. It doesn't have
     much effect on him. He turns his wrath on her.

33 INT. LIBRARY - DAY   33

Buffy fights Philip. She "lets" Philip back her towards the   *
book cage -- actually setting him up.

Ethan jumps the front desk, makes a run for the library doors   *
as Xander, Cordelia, Willow and Jenny enter.

                    BUFFY
               (to Xander, re: Ethan)
          Don't let him get away!

Xander grabs Ethan and a small wrestling match ensues.

Philip lunges at Buffy, she ducks under his big arms and
boots him into the cage, slamming and locking the cage door
on him.

Ethan breaks free of Xander, makes a bee-line for the exit,
and is stopped by Cordelia, who kicks him in the knee and
sends him to the floor.

                    XANDER
          That'll teach you to mess with me
          when I've got a... girl.

                              DISSOLVE TO:

34 INT. LIBRARY - A LITTLE LATER - DAY   34

Philip paces in the cage, looking very dead and scary.
Willow watches him from a safe distance. As do Xander,
Cordelia, Jenny and Ethan.

                    WILLOW
          I'm not getting close enough to feel
          his pulse, but I've gotta say he
          looks pretty dead.

                    XANDER
          Except for the walking around and
          attacking Buffy part.

                                        CONTINUED

34 CONTINUED: 34

> ETHAN
> He's dead.
>> (to Phil)
> Sorry, Philip. Really I am.

> BUFFY
> You know him?

> ETHAN
> Knew him.

> CORDELIA
> Hey, you don't speak until we tell
> you to speak.

> BUFFY
> Uh, Cordelia, I did tell him to speak.

           *

Giles RUSHES in.

> GILES
> Is everyone all right?

> CORDELIA
> Super. I kicked a guy.

           *

> JENNY
> We're okay.

> XANDER
> Dead guy there interrupted our
> tutorial.
>> (to Philip)
> Been meaning to thank you for that.

Philip makes a terrible sound in his throat. Xander takes a
GIANT step back. Giles studies Philip.

CONTINUED

34 CONTINUED: (2)   34

                    GILES
          It... can't be.

                    ETHAN
          Oh yes it can. Hello, Ripper.

                    GILES
          I thought I told you to leave town.

                    ETHAN
          You did. I didn't. Shop's lease is
          paid through the end of the month.

Cordelia turns to Xander.

                    CORDELIA
          Why'd he call him Ripper?

Giles grabs Ethan. Pretty roughly. The gang's never seen
him like this before.

                    GILES
          You should have left when I told you!

                    CORDELIA
          Oh.

                    GILES
          You've put these people in danger.
          These are people I care about.

Again Cordelia turns to Xander.

                    CORDELIA
          Wow, even me?

Xander gives a quick shake of his head: "no".

                    ETHAN
          If you care so much about them why
          didn't you leave town. I know you've
          been having the dreams, I have, we
          both know what's coming.

Giles glares at Ethan, then lets him go. Buffy moves next to
him.

                    BUFFY
          What dreams, what's going on?

A beat.

                                              CONTINUED

34 CONTINUED: (3)   34

                         GILES
               I...

                         ETHAN
               Tell her, Ripper.

Buffy looks from Ethan to Giles.

                         BUFFY
               Giles?

SUDDENLY: Philip KICKS open the cage door. Hurls Calendar
into the wall. She hits her head and FALLS to the ground,
unconscious.

                         GILES
               Jenny!

Ethan looks truly frightened of Philip and runs for the door.

                         ETHAN
               Nooo!

Willow and Cordelia scramble out of the way as Buffy punches
and kicks Philip.

Xander slides a book cart behind Philip. Buffy stomps Philip
into it. He goes over the book cart and lands on the floor.
He starts to get up. Buffy moves in for further carnage, but
Philip's body begins to shake.

                                                              *

Philip collapses on the floor and (C.G.I. EFFECT) liquefies.
They react.

                         WILLOW
               That's something you don't see every
               day.

                         CORDELIA
               Oh my god! I'll be in therapy till
               I'm thirty!

                                                    CONTINUED

34 CONTINUED: (4)   34

The liquid moves across the floor. Eerie. Giles has knelt
down, the unconscious Jenny cradled in his arms.

TIGHTER ANGLE - No one notices Jenny's hand on the floor as
a tiny trickle of the liquid touches it. Her hand TWITCHES.

Calendar starts to come to.

                    GILES
              Jenny?

                    JENNY
              (holding her head)
              Ow...

                    GILES
              Careful, careful. Can you stand?

                    JENNY
              I think so.

Giles helps her to her feet.

                    CORDELIA
              (sotto; to Xander)
              This is what happens when you have
              school on Saturday.

Calendar gets her balance.

                                                              *

                    GILES
              Here, lean on me.

And she does. Her arms go around him. He holds her for a
beat.

                    GILES (cont'd)
              It'll be all right...

                    JENNY
              Promise?

                    GILES
              I promise.

Over his shoulder, we see her face. She seems to relax a
little at his words.

                                                  CONTINUED

34 CONTINUED: (5)   34

                         JENNY
              I believe you.

Then we (and only we) see her eyes. As THEY begin to GLOW.

                                   BLACK OUT.

                    END OF ACT TWO

ACT THREE

35 INT. LIBRARY - A MOMENT LATER - DAY   35

Calendar (who looks and acts very Calendar-like for the
moment) leans on the table, wash cloth to her head. Giles is
next to her.

          GILES
  How's your head?

          JENNY
  Throbbing.

Buffy moves near Giles. He looks at her, uncomfortable,
tense.

                                              *

          BUFFY
  Giles, what's going on?

          GILES
  It's... complicated, Buffy, and
  frankly it's private.

          BUFFY
  I don't care from private, I care
  from dead guys attacking us, I care
  from you Lost Weekending in your
  apartment.

          GILES
  I wasn't... I just had to work out
  a solution.

          BUFFY
  Solution is good. Why don't we
  share? What's the mark of Eyghon?

Jenny moans a little, rubs her head with the washcloth.

          GILES
  This is not your battle, and as your
  Watcher, I'm telling you in no
  uncertain terms: stay out of it. I've
  got to get Jenny home.

          JENNY
  Home. That sounds so good right now.

                              CONTINUED

35 CONTINUED: 35

        Giles takes her arm and walks her to the door. They head
        out, Buffy staring hard after them.

                                                                        *

        Buffy takes control, handing out orders:

                          BUFFY
                We have work to do. Willow, I want   *
                you to find out anything and
                everything you can about the mark of
                Eyghon.

                          WILLOW
                So what Giles just said about staying
                out of it --

                          BUFFY
                Thrill, as I ignore it completely.
                He needs our help and he's going to
                get it.

                          WILLOW
                I can try the net, but the mark of
                Eyghon sounds like a Giles and his
                books kind of deal.

                          BUFFY
                So we hit the books.

        Buffy follows Willow, as she heads for the books.

                          BUFFY (cont'd)
                Xander, how do you feel about rifling
                through Giles' personal files, see if
                you can shed some light.

                          XANDER
                I feel pretty good about it. Does
                that make me a sociopath?

        Buffy hits the books herself. Cordelia moves next to her,
        impatient. Buffy finally notices her.

                          BUFFY
                What?

                          CORDELIA
                What about me? I care about Giles.

                                                            CONTINUED

35 CONTINUED: (2)   35

> BUFFY
> Work with Xander.

> CORDELIA
> Well, when I say "care", I mean --

> BUFFY
> Cordelia.

> CORDELIA
> Okay, okay.

CUT TO:

36 INT. GILES' APARTMENT - DUSK (OKAY, NIGHT)   36

Jenny and Giles.

> JENNY
> Thanks for bringing me here. I'm not
> quite ready to be home alone just yet.

Giles nods, hands her a glass. She drinks, makes a face.

> JENNY (cont'd)
> It's strong.
>   (drinks some more)
> It's helping.

> GILES
> You need it after what you've been
> through.

She nods innocently.

> GILES (cont'd)
> Jenny, I'm so sorry about this. I
> never meant for you to get involved
> in any of this.

> JENNY
> So I got involved. That's what
> happens when two people... get
> involved.

She moves closer. It looks for a moment like he might kiss
her, then:

> GILES
> I will have to get you home, soon.
> It's not -- I'm not a safe person to
> be around right now.

CONTINUED

36 CONTINUED: 36

                          JENNY
               Nothing's safe in this world, Rupert.
               Don't you know that by now?

She looks up at him. And for the first time he seems to
relax a little, Jenny's made him feel comfortable.

                                              CUT TO:

37 INT. LIBRARY - NIGHT   37

Willow plows through an UNBELIEVABLE STACK of Giles' books on
the long table. She suddenly hits one of the books rather
hard.

                          WILLOW
               Ah! Aha! It's not Egyptian it's
               Etruscan, mistaken for Egyptian by
               the design pattern but any fool can
               see it pre-dates their iconology...

Willow shows Buffy a DRAWING IN THE BOOK, THE MARK OF EYGHON.
The demon as we've seen it in the tattoos.

                          WILLOW (cont'd)
               Look at this: the Mark Of Eyghon,
               worn by his initiates.
                    (reads)
               "Eyghon, also called the Sleepwalker,
               can only exist in this reality by
               possessing an unconscious host.
               Temporary possession imbues the host
               with a euphoric feeling of power."

                          BUFFY
               What about not temporary?

                          WILLOW
               "Unless the proper rituals are
               observed, the possession is
               permanent, and Eyghon will be born
               from within the host."

                          CORDELIA
               I'm guessing, "Eew."

                                              CONTINUED

37 CONTINUED: 37

                    WILLOW
          Hey, listen. "Once called, Eyghon
          can also take possession of the dead,
          but its demonic energy soon
          disintegrates the host and it must
          jump to the nearest dead or
          unconscious person to continue
          living."

                    BUFFY
          I still don't understand what this
          has to do with Giles.

                    WILLOW
               (has been skimming)
          Well, I don't know about Giles, but
          ancient sects used to induce
          possession for bacchanals and orgies.

                    XANDER
          Okay, "Giles" and "orgies" in the
          same sentence. Coulda lived without
          that.

                    BUFFY
          Wait a minute. The dead guy. He's
          all puddly now.

                    CORDELIA
          So the demon is gone. There was no
          one dead to jump into. I mean, we're
          all not dead, right?

                    BUFFY
          No one dead...

She looks at Xander, who picks up her train of thought.

                    XANDER
          But someone unconscious.

                                        CUT TO:

38 INT. GILES' APARTMENT - NIGHT   38

CLOSE ON: a phone jack as a HAND rips the jack out of the   *
wall.

Jenny drops the wire (which we see leads to the now useless
phone) to the floor as Giles enters from the kitchen with two
cups of tea.

                                                  CONTINUED

38 CONTINUED: 38

                    GILES
          What was that?

                    JENNY
          What was what?

                    GILES
          I thought I heard something.

                    JENNY
          I didn't.
                    (takes tea)
          Thanks.

                    GILES
          Drink it and then I'll take you home.

                    JENNY
          You could take me home...
                    (sets tea down)
          ...or you could take advantage of me
          in my weakened state.

Off Giles,

                                        CUT TO:

39 INT. GILES' OFFICE - NIGHT   39

    The desk and files are a mess. Xander is pouring through
    them. Willow and Cordelia watch Buffy on the phone.

                    BUFFY
          Thank you, operator.

    Buffy slams the phone down.

                    BUFFY (cont'd)
          No answer at Ms. Calendar's and
          Giles' line is out of order. I'm
          getting over there.

                                        CUT TO:

40 INT. GILES' APARTMENT - NIGHT   40

    Giles and Jenny, as before.

                    GILES
          Jenny, I am attracted to you...

                                        CONTINUED

40 CONTINUED: 40

                        JENNY
          Good.

                        GILES
          But this isn't the right time.

                        JENNY
          There's never been a better time.

She puts her arms around him. They kiss. He gives in for a
beat, then pulls back.

                        GILES
          No, it's not right, I'd be taking
          advantage.

Jenny smiles. Not a particularly pleasant smile.

                        JENNY
          God, you don't change, do you.

                        GILES
          Uh...?

                        JENNY
          "It's not right, wouldn't be
          proper..."

And then her voice changes -- merges actually, with a DEEP
MAN'S VOICE. A scary voice. That of a demon.

                        JENNY (cont'd)
                    (demon voice)
          "...people might get hurt."

Giles tries to take a step back, alarmed. But Calendar's
hand holds his arm like iron.

                        GILES
          What's...?

                        JENNY
                    (demon-voiced)
          "You're like a woman, Ripper, you cry
          at every funeral. You never had the
          strength for me, you don't deserve
          me. But guess what, you've got me --
          UNDER YOUR SKIN!

She PULLS him close. He tries to resist but she's suddenly
very strong. She kisses him hard on the mouth.

                                                    CONTINUED

40 CONTINUED: (2)   40

                                                              *

And now we see the patches of her skin where the DEMON EYGHON
has begun to break through. Putrid flesh, sores, devil's
skin. Ridges on her forehead. Not a pretty girl.

                                                              *

                    DEMON JENNY
          Was it good for you?

She grabs him and RAMS HIS HEAD into a wall. She holds him
up to her face.

                    DEMON JENNY (cont'd)
          You never had the stomach. But
          that's okay, I'm about to rip it out.

She hurls him into a wall.

The front door is KNOCKED OPEN, lock splintering. Buffy
comes flying in. Demon Jenny turns and hisses. Buffy takes
a moment to absorb the hideousness of what she's seeing, then
sends Demon Jenny sprawling backwards with a KICK to the
midsection.

Buffy stands in front of Giles, blocking Demon Jenny's way to
him.

                    BUFFY
          Back off. Just stay back.

Demon Calendar looks at Buffy, then at Giles.

                    DEMON JENNY
                (laughs)
          Three down, two to go! Be seeing you.

She DIVES through a window.

41 EXT. GILES APARTMENT - NIGHT   41

    (PRODUCTION NOTE: This is actually a SMALL facade with a
    second story window on stage -- until the budget kills it --
    which Demon Jenny comes flying out of and drops from sight.)

42   INT. GILES APARTMENT - NIGHT   42

Buffy kneels down to Giles, who is badly injured. Blood runs
down his forehead, and his arm is useless.

                    BUFFY
          Are you all right?

                    GILES   .
          Jenny... Oh, God...

                    BUFFY
          Giles, how do we stop this thing?

                    GILES
          God, what have I done?

                    BUFFY
          Talk to me! Giles, you're scaring
          me.

There is real helpless fear in his surrogate daughter's
voice. He comes to, stares at her -- but can do no more.
Finally:

                    GILES
          I'm sorry...

                    BUFFY
               (hurt anger)
          Don't be sorry! Be Giles! Come on,
          we fight monsters. They show up,
          they scare us, I beat them up, and
          they leave. This isn't any different.

                    GILES
          It is different.

                    BUFFY
          Because you don't know how to stop it.

                    GILES
          Because I created it.

                                        CUT TO:

43   INT. LIBRARY - NIGHT   43

Xander enters from Giles' office.

                    WILLOW
          Did you find anything?

                                        CONTINUED

43 CONTINUED: 43

> XANDER
> The most meticulous banking and phone
> records you've ever seen, and this.

He pulls out a PHOTO and shows it to the others.

> XANDER (cont'd)
> Apparently Giles wasn't always Giles.

> WILLOW
> That's Giles?

> CORDELIA
> Wow, was he like in a band?

> XANDER
> Once upon a time boys and girls,
> Giles was us.

On the PHOTO: GILES as a young PUNK TEENAGER. Circa 70's.

> GILES (V.O.)
> I was twenty-one...

                                                    CUT TO:

44   INT. GILES APARTMENT - NIGHT   44

Buffy has gotten Giles to the couch where he sits in the
darkened apartment, telling her his story. She's bandaging
his arm.

> GILES
> Studying history at Oxford and of
> course the occult by night. I hated
> it. The boring grind of school, the
> pressure of my "destiny". So I
> dropped out. I went to London, fell
> in with the worse crowd that would
> have me. We practiced magicks.
> Small stuff, for pleasure of gain.
> And then Ethan and I discovered
> something a little bigger.

> BUFFY
> Eyghon.

> GILES
> Yes. We put one of us into a deep
> sleep and the others would summon
> him. It was an extraordinary high.
> God, we were fools.

                                                    CONTINUED

44 CONTINUED: 44

                      BUFFY
You couldn't control it.

                      GILES
One of us, Randall, he lost control.
Eyghon took him whole. We tried to
exorcise the demon from Randall, but
it killed him. We killed him.

                      BUFFY
God...

                      GILES
We thought we were free of the demon
after that. But it's back. And one
by one it will kill us all.

                      BUFFY
Three down, two to go.   *

Giles nods.

                    BUFFY (cont'd)
Then it's going after Ethan. I
better beat it there.

                      GILES
We better.

                      BUFFY
I. You're barely mobile and speed is
of the serious essence.

                      GILES
Buffy, I don't know how to stop it
without... without killing Jenny.

                      BUFFY
I got the guys working on it. I'll
try to contain her till we can figure
something.

She starts out.

                      GILES
Buffy!

She stops.

                    GILES (cont'd)
I'm sorry.

                                    CONTINUED

44 CONTINUED: (2)   44

                         BUFFY
          I know.

She goes.

                                              CUT TO:

45 EXT. SUNNYDALE STREET - NIGHT   45

A LITTLE DOG trots down the sidewalk, HAPPY and CAREFREE.

REVEAL the dog is being walked by its owner, a MAN equally
happy and carefree. The dog starts SNARLING at something.

                         MAN
          Whoa there, Spritzer. It's okay.

The dog BARKS uncontrollably at someone in the SHADOWS.

                         MAN (cont'd)
                    (to dog)
          Come on, there's nothing to be afraid
          of.
                    (then, to unseen
                     person)
          Spritzer's a friendly little guy. He
          really likes people.

The person steps out of the shadows: it's DEMON CALENDAR, who
looks even more Hellish than before. Her flesh hangs
loosely, the sores on her face have opened up, and the
forehead ridges protrude further out. She speaks in her
demon voice:

                         DEMON CALENDAR
          I really like dogs.

The man becomes less happy and carefree. Demon Calendar
SNATCHES the leash from his hand. The man slowly backs away.

                         MAN
          Spritzer...

The man's eyes go wide. He turns and BOLTS for his life. We
WATCH HIM GO as we hear:

The dog BARKING. Then YELPING. Then a more horrible sound:
MUNCHING.

Then NOTHING.

                                              DISSOLVE TO:

46   INT. ABANDONED COSTUME SHOP - LATER THAT NIGHT   46

Buffy comes inside and looks around. The place is DARK,
EMPTY, and spooky, dress mannequins break up the space,
looking like so many dead people.

                    BUFFY
               Ethan...

Buffy cautiously moves further in. She hears a NOISE and
SPINS around. Nothing. Or did something move behind one of
the mannequins?

                    BUFFY (cont'd)
               I'm not here to hurt you... I'm sorry
               to say. Giles told me everything.
               It's coming for you. We've got to
               stop it.

Ethan APPEARS behind her.

                    ETHAN
               And you came to protect me. I'm
               touched.

Buffy spins around.

                    BUFFY
               Don't worry, it's nothing personal:
               to protect Giles I have to protect
               you.

                    ETHAN
               How does Ripper inspire such goodness?

                    BUFFY
               Because he's Giles.

                    ETHAN
               And I'm not. Still, lucky me.

                    BUFFY
               Lucky you.

                    ETHAN
               Well, we can't run. Eyghon will find   *
               us. This mark might as well be a   *
               homing beacon.   *

                    BUFFY
               That's all right. I'm not big on   *
               running anyway.   *

                    ETHAN
               Aren't we manly.

                                                    CONTINUED

46 CONTINUED: 46

                         BUFFY
          One of us is. You're gonna hide till   *
          it's over.

                         ETHAN
          Excellent plan.   *

                         BUFFY
          Is there a way in through the back?   *

                         ETHAN   *
          There's a door, but it's locked. I   *
          think it's solid.   *

                         BUFFY   *
          Well, we can set you up back there.   *
          Come on.   *

                         ETHAN
          Oh, no...

                                            CONTINUED

46 CONTINUED: 46

He gestures for her to go. Buffy moves towards the back.

Ethan steps behind her. And now we see the board in his
hands. Which he beings up sharply and cracks her on the head
with. Hard. She falls to the ground. He stares down at her.

                    ETHAN (cont'd)
          ...ladies first.

                              BLACK OUT.

          END OF ACT THREE

ACT FOUR

47 INT. ABANDONED COSTUME SHOP - LATER - NIGHT   47

PUSH PAST the creepy mannequin shapes and ETHAN (whistling a
jaunty tune as he works) to BUFFY, lying face down on a long,
narrow table. Her ankles are TIED TOGETHER, and her arms are   *
wrapped around the table with her wrists TIED TOGETHER   *
underneath it. Ethan finishes tying her as she comes to.   *

                    ETHAN
          Wakey, wakey. You don't want to miss
          the fun.

                    BUFFY
          What fun?

                    ETHAN
          Your initiation.

                    BUFFY
          You know what? I'm not real
          interested in joining your club.

                    ETHAN
          Too late. I already voted you in.
          I hope you appreciate this is nothing
          personal, Buffy. I actually kind of
          like you. It's just...

He grabs a LARGE, ominous-looking NEEDLE off a tray and dips
it in ink.

                    ETHAN (cont'd)
          I like myself more. You know, if you
          look at it karmically, this is very
          big for your soul: you're taking my
          place with the demon, giving so that
          others may live.

                    BUFFY
          I'm going to kill you. Will that
          blow the whole karma thing?

He pulls Buffy's hair away, revealing the back of her neck.

                    ETHAN
          Now, you might feel a slight sting at
          first. But that'll go away once the
          searing pain kicks in.

He begins CARVING THE TATTOO into the back of Buffy's neck.

                                        CONTINUED

47 CONTINUED: 47

ANGLE: BUFFY'S FACE

as she grimaces and grits her teeth.

                ETHAN (cont'd)
    You can go ahead and scream.

                              CUT TO:

48 INT. LIBRARY - NIGHT   48

Willow is still absorbed in books. As she reads, she brings
a cup of tea into frame, sips. Cordelia and Xander scour the
books.

                WILLOW
    We have to figure out how to kill
    this thing. And we have to do it
    fast.

                XANDER
      (re: book)
    Hot lava.

                WILLOW
    That's for a heretic.

                XANDER
    Oh, yeah. Okay, bury a potato. No,
    that's for warts.
      (looking at the cover)
    Who writes these things?

                CORDELIA
    Duhh. I've got the solution, right
    here.
      (points to her book)
    To kill a demon, cut its head off.

                XANDER
    Great work, Cor.

                CORDELIA
    You could have done it -- not really.

                XANDER
    Yeah, we'll just find Ms. Calendar
    and then we'll decapitate her. She
    can be the first headless computer
    teacher, think anyone'll notice?

                            CONTINUED

                    CORDELIA
          You know what you need, Xander --
          besides a year's supply of acne
          cream -- a brain.

                    XANDER
          That's it, twelve years of you, I'm
          snapping. I don't care you're a
          girl, I'm throwing down.
                    (gets in a fight
                     stance)
          Come on.

                    CORDELIA
          I've seen you fight, don't think I
          can't take you.

                    XANDER
          Give it your best shot!

Willow has a huge book in her hands which she slams down on
the table in front of them. It's loud and it gets their
attention.

                    WILLOW
          Heyyy! We don't have time for this.
          Our friends are in trouble. Now we
          have to put our heads together and
          get them out of it. And if you two
          aren't with me a hundred and ten per
          cent then get the hell out of my
          library!

She points at the door, dramatically. Xander and Cordelia
hang their heads, chastened.

                    CORDELIA
          We're sorry.

                    XANDER
          We'll be good.

                    WILLOW
          We've done the research, we've got to
          think how to use it.

                    XANDER
          Okay, what if we find another dead
          body for the demon to jump into?

                    CORDELIA
                    (picking up on it)
          Yeah. At the cemetary.

                                              CONTINUED

48 CONTINUED: (2)   48

> WILLOW
> That won't kill the demon; it'll just
> give it a change of scenery.

Xander and Cordelia sag.

> WILLOW (cont'd)
> Oh! Oh! Oh! I've got it!

She runs out the door. Xander and Cordelia start to follow.

> XANDER
> She's good.

                              CUT TO:

49 INT. ABANDONED COSTUME SHOP - A BIT LATER - NIGHT   49

Ethan wipes the back of Buffy's neck with a cloth and we see
the completed TATTOO, the now familiar mark of Eyghon.

> ETHAN
> Perhaps I missed my calling as an
> artist.

> BUFFY
> Listen to me, Ethan. This is a BAD   *
> IDEA. You're dealing with something   *
> very dangerous.   *

> ETHAN
> But this'll throw Eyghon off my   *
> scent.   *

> BUFFY   *
> I'm not talking about Eyghon.   *

Ethan reaches towards the tray and grabs a bottle of
ACID. Buffy looks alarmed, struggles with her bonds.

> ETHAN
> Gosh, you are spunky. Relax, I'm   *
> done with you. It's my turn now...

Ethan smiles at her, then pours acid on his own tattoo. Of
course we cut tastefully away as he GRIMACES and MOANS as he
works.

                                                        CONTINUED

49 CONTINUED: 49

    ANGLE: BENEATH THE TABLE

    Buffy searches around with her fingers. She feels a NAIL
    protruding slightly from the inside edge. She begins to dig
    her fingernail into the wood, trying to jar the nail loose.

                                           CUT TO:

50 INT. GILES APARTMENT - NIGHT   50

    Giles stumbles toward the door, putting his coat over his
    shoulder. He's very WOOZY from Demon Jenny's beating. He
    goes up a step or two, then stumbles, falls to the floor and
    we FLASH TO:

    ANOTHER SERIES OF VISIONS

    (production note: these are taken from scenes we'll be
    shooting)

    1) The PHOTO of young Giles.

    2) The TATTOO.

    3) The possessed CREEPY CULT GUY, all demony, engulfed in the
    flames.

    4) Deirdre (Corpse Woman) SCREAMING.   *

    5) A SHATTERING WINDOW as DEAD PHILIP CRASHES through.

    6) DEMON CALENDAR making her way through the DARK NIGHT.

    7) Buffy, tied to the table.

    8) The TATTOO on the back of her neck.

    Giles WAKES UP with a jolt.

                    GILES
            Ethan...Oh, no...

    With great effort, he rises, stumbles to the door, and
    STAGGERS OUT.

                                             CUT TO:

51 INT. ABANDONED COSTUME SHOP - LATER - NIGHT   51

    Ethan has finished burning the tattoo off of his arm.

                                             CONTINUED

51 CONTINUED: 51

ANGLE: BENEATH THE TABLE

Buffy has the nail out and is using it to cut the rope that   *
binds her wrists.

ETHAN wraps a bandage around his arm.

                    ETHAN
          I hate to mutilate and run, but...

He heads for the door, stops, seeing:

ANGLE: THE DOOR

An EERIE GREEN LIGHT spills from beneath it as the door
starts to RUMBLE. Ethan backs away. Fast.

The door SHOOTS OPEN, seemingly on its own. Demon Calendar
stands there, bathed in light.

Demon Calendar steps inside. The door SHUTS behind her as
she moves towards Ethan.

                    DEMON JENNY
          It is your time.

Ethan stands frozen. Demon Calendar gets nose-to-nose with
him. Then JERKS her head and STARES right at Buffy. And
leaps.

ANGLE: BENEATH THE TABLE

Buffy cuts through the rope.   *

Buffy ROLLS off the table as Demon Calendar lands on it.
Buffy rocks onto her back and UPENDS the table by KICKING IT
with her still-bound feet. Demon Calendar falls away.

Buffy RIPS the rope off her ankles and stands to face Demon   *
Calendar, with the table between them. Demon Calendar picks
up the table and uses it to push Buffy back, PINNING HER
against the wall. Buffy strains to escape. She's trapped.

                    GILES (O.S.)
          Eyghon!

REVEAL Giles is there.

                    GILES
          Take me.

Demon Calendar HEAVES the table aside. It crashes and
SPLINTERS near Ethan, who now crouches in a corner.

                                                      CONTINUED

> GILES (cont'd)
> Buffy, get out of here!

Demon Calendar goes for Giles.

> BUFFY
> No!

Buffy tries to move between them. Demon Calendar raises her hand and TOUCHES HER FINGER to Buffy's face.

A SURGE OF ENERGY rushes through the touch, and Buffy is THROWN across the room.

Demon Calendar TOSSES Giles to the ground and STRADDLES him.

> DEMON CALENDAR
> I've been waiting a long time to do
> this.

Suddenly, Demon Calendar is TACKLED off Giles --

by ANGEL.

Willow, Xander, and Cordelia RUN in just in time to see Angel STRANGLING THE LIFE OUT of Demon Calendar. Giles starts toward her, but Willow stops him.

> GILES
> He's killing her.

> WILLOW
> Trust me. This is going to work...

Demon Calendar claws at Angel's hands as she GASPS for breath. She looks up at Angel. Their eyes lock.

Demon Calendar HOWLS out in pain as Angel is THROWN off her. She rolls away, COUGHING and we see:

She's back to being JENNY.

> CORDELIA
> Did we kill it?

Angel CRIES OUT. His eyes GLOW.

> BUFFY
> It's in Angel!

CONTINUED

51 CONTINUED: (3)   51

                         WILLOW
                    (much less
                     confidently)
          This is going to work.

They watch as Angel's FACE MORPHS:

The Demon. The Vampire. Regular Angel. Alternating between
the three as an INTERNAL BATTLE takes place.

Finally, the demon SCREAMS OUT and FADES AWAY.

Angel falls to the ground. Buffy and Willow rush over to
him. Ethan takes the opportunity to sneak out.

Giles has recovered and struggles to his feet. He goes to
Calendar and takes her in his arms.

                         GILES
          Jenny...?

                         JENNY
          Rupert.

                         GILES
          It's okay. I've got you.

Buffy and Willow help Angel to his feet, Buffy putting it
together:

                         BUFFY
          You knew that if the demon was in
          danger it would jump into the nearest
          dead guy.

Willow nods, even smiles.

                         ANGEL
          I put it in danger.

                         WILLOW
          And it jumped.

                         ANGEL
          But I've had a demon inside me for a
          couple hundred years just waiting for
          a good fight.

                         BUFFY
          Winner and still champion.

                                                   CONTINUED

51 CONTINUED: (4)   51

                         XANDER
                Uh, I think that Ethan guy
                disappeared.

                         BUFFY
                Darn. I really wanted to hit him
                till he bled.

                         CORDELIA
                Well, at least it's over.

Buffy looks at:

ANGLE: GILES AND JENNY

as he helps her to the door. It's not over for him.

A52 EXT. SUNNYDALE HIGH - DAY   A52

                Xander, Buffy, and Willow walk along.

                         BUFFY
                The worst thing is, I was saving up
                for some very important shoes. Now
                I gotta blow my allowance getting
                this stupid tattoo removed. I just
                hope mom doesn't see it first.

                         XANDER
                Putting the demon into Angel was
                pretty brill, Will.

                         WILLOW
                I wasn't sure it would work.

                         BUFFY
                But it did.

                         XANDER
                Like a charm.

                         BUFFY
                Maybe you should consider a career as
                a Watcher.

                         WILLOW
                Oh no. I don't think I could take the
                stress.

                         XANDER
                And the dental plan is crap.

                                                            CONTINUED

52 CONTINUED: A52

                         WILLOW
              I don't know how Giles does it.

                         BUFFY
              I don't think he has a choice.

She looks off at:

ANGLE: GILES

as he hurries to enter a school building.

52 INT. HALL - DAY   B52   *

Jenny enters, Giles moves to Jenny.   *

                         GILES
              Jenny. Jenny --

                         JENNY
              Rupert. Hi.

                         GILES
              I tried to call you last night. See
              how you were.

                         JENNY
              Yeah, I left the phone off the hook.
              I seem to need a lot of sleep lately.

                         GILES
              But you're alright? Is there
              something you need?

                         JENNY
                    (shakes her head)
              I'm fine. I mean, I'm not "running
              around, wind in my hair, the hills
              are alive with the Sound of Music"
              fine, but I'm coping.

                         GILES
              I would like to help.

                         JENNY
              I know.

                         GILES
              Perhaps we could talk some time.
              Have dinner, or a drink -- when
              you're feeling stronger.

                                                      CONTINUED

B52   CONTINUED: B52

                            JENNY
                Sure. Some time.

        He moves to put his hand on her arm. She flinches, jerking
        subtly away. He puts his arm down.

                                                    CONTINUED

B52 CONTINUED: (2)   B52

> JENNY (cont'd)
> Yeah, some time... I better get to
> class.

> GILES
> Of course.

Buffy approaches him.

> BUFFY
> How is she?

> GILES
> The hills are not alive.

> BUFFY
> I'm sorry to hear that... I think...

> GILES
> I don't imagine she'll ever really
> forgive me. Maybe she shouldn't.

> BUFFY
> Maybe you should.

> GILES
> I never wanted you to see that side
> of me.

> BUFFY
> I'm not gonna lie. It was scary.   *
> I'm used to you being, you know, The   *
> Grown-up. And then I find out that   *
> you're a person.   *

> GILES   *
> Most grown-ups are.   *

> BUFFY   *
> Who would've thought?   *

> GILES   *
> Some of them are even very short-   *
> sighted, foolish people.   *

> BUFFY   *
> So after all this time it turns out   *
> we do have something in common.   *
> Which, apart from being a little   *
> weird... is kind of okay.   *

He is quiet -- too grateful to say anything just yet.

                                                    CONTINUED

B52 CONTINUED: (3)   B52

                    BUFFY (cont'd)
          I think we're supposed to be
          training, right?

                    GILES
          Uh, yes. Need to concentrate on your
          flexibility.

                    BUFFY
                (holds up CD)
          I got the perfect music.

                                              CONTINUED

A52 CONTINUED: (3)   A52

He eyes the CD.

                    BUFFY (cont'd)
          Go on, you know you want to say it.

A moment, then he dives in:

                    GILES
          That isn't music, it's just
          meaningless sounds.

                    BUFFY
          There. Feel better?

                    GILES
          Yes, thank you.

They head off.

                    GILES (cont'd)
          The Bay City Rollers, now that's
          music.

                    BUFFY
                (an "I don't know
                 you" look)
          Oh, god...

                                        BLACK OUT.

                    END OF SHOW

BUFFY THE VAMPIRE SLAYER

"What's My Line? - Part One"

Written By

Howard Gordon and Marti Noxon

Directed By

David Solomon

<u>SHOOTING SCRIPT</u>

October 1, 1997
October 6, 1997 (Blue Pages)
October 7, 1997 (Pink Pages)
October 8, 1997 (Yellow Pages)

BUFFY THE VAMPIRE SLAYER

"What's My Line? - Part One"

CAST LIST

BUFFY SUMMERS.......................... Sarah Michelle Gellar
XANDER HARRIS......................... Nicholas Brendon
RUPERT GILES.......................... Anthony S. Head
WILLOW ROSENBERG...................... Alyson Hannigan
CORDELIA CHASE........................ Charisma Carpenter
ANGEL................................. David Boreanaz

MR. SNYDER............................ Armin Shimerman
SPIKE................................. James Marsters
DRUSILLA.............................. Juliet Landau
OZ.................................... Seth Green
KENDRA................................ Bianca Lawson
DALTON...............................*Eric Saiet
SUIT MAN.............................. Michael Rothhaar
OCTARUS...............................
MR. PFISTER........................... Kelly Connell
MRS. KALISH........................... P.B. Hutton
WILLY................................. Savero Guerra
BAGGAGE HANDLER.......................

BUFFY THE VAMPIRE SLAYER

"What's My Line? - Part One"

SET LIST

INTERIORS

SUNNYDALE HIGH SCHOOL
    HALL
    LIBRARY
    LOUNGE
BUFFY'S HOUSE
    BUFFY'S BEDROOM
    LIVING ROOM
FACTORY
    DRUSILLA'S BEDROOM
MAUSOLEUM
767 CARGO HOLD
SKATING RINK
MRS. KALISH'S HOUSE
ANGEL'S APARTMENT
    FOYER
WILLY'S ALIBI ROOM
    STORAGE ROOM

EXTERIORS

SUNNYDALE HIGH SCHOOL
    *PALM COURT
CEMETERY
BUS STATION
NEIGHBORHOOD
BUFFY'S HOUSE
AIRPORT (STOCK)

BUFFY THE VAMPIRE SLAYER

"What's My Line?... Part One"

TEASER

1 INT. SCHOOL LOUNGE - DAY   1

FADE UP ON BANNER - "CAREER FAIR STARTS TOMORROW"

CAMERA pans down.

A GUIDANCE COUNSELOR sits behind a table from which a sign
hangs - "VOCATIONAL APTITUDE TESTS."

WILLOW grabs a test and a number 2 pencil from the table -
moves to BUFFY and XANDER, who sit filling out their forms.

                    XANDER
               (reading)
          "Are you a people person or do you
          prefer keeping your own company?"
          What if I'm a people person who keeps
          his own company by default?

                    BUFFY
          So - mark "none of the above."

                    XANDER
          There is no box for "none of the
          above." That would introduce too
          many variables into their mushroom
          head, number-crunching little world.

                    WILLOW
          I'm sensing bitterness.

                    XANDER
          It's just - these people can't tell
          from one multiple choice test what
          we're supposed to do for the rest of
          our lives. It's ridiculous.

                    WILLOW
          I'm kind of curious to find out what
          sort of career I could have.

                    XANDER
          And suck all the spontaneity out of
          being young and stupid? I'd rather
          live in the dark.

                                                   CONTINUED

1 CONTINUED: 1

                         WILLOW
            We won't be young forever.

                         XANDER
            I'll always be stupid.
                  (beat)
            Okay, let's not all rush to
            disagree...

CORDELIA, trailed by a few Cordettes, flounces by - test in   *
hand.   *

                         CORDELIA   *
                  (reading)   *
            "I aspire to help my fellow man."   *
            Check.   *

She marks her test.   *

                         CORDELIA   *
            I mean, as long as he's not, like,   *
            smelly or dirty or something gross-   *

Xander, who has overheard this, chimes in.   *

                         XANDER   *
            Cordelia Chase, always ready to offer   *
            a helping hand to the rich and pretty.   *

                         CORDELIA   *
            Which, lucky me, excludes you --   *
            twice!   *

She moves off, the Cordettes tittering. Xander stares after   *
her.   *

                         XANDER   *
            Is murder always a crime?

Buffy looks up from her test.   *

                         BUFFY
            Do I like shrubs?   *

                         XANDER
            That's between you and your God.

                         BUFFY
                  (to Willow)
            What'd you put?

                                                      CONTINUED

1 CONTINUED: (2)   1

                    WILLOW
          I came down on the side of shrubs.

                    BUFFY
          Go shrubs. Okay.
                    (puts down pencil)
          I shouldn't even be bothering with
          this. It's all moot-ville for me.
          No matter what my aptitude test
          says - I already know my deal.

                    XANDER
          Yep. High risk, sub-minimum wage...

                    BUFFY
                    (holds up pencil)
          Pointy wooden things.

                    WILLOW
          So why are you even taking the test?

                    BUFFY
          It's Principal Snyder's "hoop" of the
          week. He's not happy unless I'm
          jumping. Believe me, I wouldn't be
          here otherwise--

                                        CONTINUED

1 CONTINUED: (3)   1

                         WILLOW
          You're not even a teensy weensy bit
          curious about what kind of career you
          could have had? I mean, if you
          weren't already the Slayer and all.

                         BUFFY
                    (snapping)
          Do the words "sealed" and "fate" ring
          any bells for you, Will? Why go
          there?

Willow looks stung by Buffy's tone.

                         XANDER
                    (to Buffy)
          You know - with that kind of attitude
          you could have had a bright future
          as an employee of the DMV.

                         BUFFY
          I'm sorry... It's just - unless hell
          freezes over and every vamp in
          Sunnydale puts in for early
          retirement - I'd say my future is
          pretty much a non-issue.

                                        CUT TO:

2 INT. FACTORY - NIGHT   2

Speaking of vamps... Here's DRUSILLA - wrapped in a black
shawl and looking even paler than usual. She stands at one
end of the long dining table, laying out TAROT CARDS. She is
humming, swaying.   *

                                                                 *

ANGLE TO INCLUDE SPIKE

At the other end of the table. He PACES ANXIOUSLY HOLDING A
LATIN/ENGLISH DICTIONARY, while ANOTHER VAMP (DALTON)
sits, carefully going over a LARGE MANUSCRIPT. DALTON has
the serious look of a scholar - sort of an anti-Giles.

                                                      CONTINUED

                    SPIKE
                 (to Dalton)
          Read it again-

                    DALTON
          I'm not sure... It could be...
          Deprimere ille bubula linter.

Spike looks through the dictionary. Then reads-

                    SPIKE
          Debase the beef... canoe.

A beat. Then he SLAMS Dalton upside the head with the
dictionary.

                    SPIKE (cont'd)
          Why does that strike me as not
          right?

Drusilla turns to him, still HUMMING, and opens her arms-

                    DRUSILLA
          Spike? Come dance...

Spike bristles at her voice.

                    SPIKE
                 (flashing)
          Give us some peace, would you? Can't
          you see I'm working?

Drusilla looks shocked at his outburst. Spike is instantly
remorseful. He moves to her.

                    SPIKE (cont'd)
          I'm sorry, kitten. It's just - this
          manuscript is supposed to hold your
          cure. But it reads like jibberish-

Drusilla turns away from him - wounded. Spike is desperate
to appease her.

                    SPIKE (cont'd)
          I'm frazzed is all. I never had the
          Latin. Even Dalton here, the big
          brain, even he can't make heads or
          tails of it-

CONTINUED

2 CONTINUED: (2)   2

                         DRUSILLA
            I - I need to change Miss Edith-

She starts to walk away, but falters. Suddenly weak - she
tries to grab the table to keep from falling. Spike RUSHES
to her side - saves her from taking a bad tumble.

He moves her gently back to a chair at the table - brushing
her shawl aside in the process. We see for the first time
that her ARMS ARE MARKED WITH LIGHT BRUISES. Spike can't   *
look at them, averts his eyes. He kneels by her, desperate.

                         SPIKE
            Forgive me. You know I can't stand
            seeing you like this...
                    (then/frustrated)
            And we're running out of time. It's
            that bloody slayer. Whenever I turn
            around she's mucking up the works-

A beat. Drusilla softens. Moved by his sincere feeling.

                         DRUSILLA
            Shhhhhhh. Shhhhhh. You'll make it
            right. I know.

Thankful for her benediction, Spike takes her hand. Kisses
it. Then he stands, full of fire - which he turns on POOR
DALTON.

                         SPIKE
            Well? Come on now. Enlighten me.

                         DALTON
                    (nervous)
            I - It looks like Latin, but it's
            not. I'm not even sure it's a
            language. Not one I can decipher,
            anyway...

Spike moves to him - furious.

                         SPIKE
            Then make it a language. Isn't that
            what a transcriber does?

                         DALTON
            Not - not exactly.

Spike GRABS DALTON. Lifts him out of his seat with ONE HAND.
Ready to do some serious damage.

                                                      CONTINUED

                         SPIKE
               I want the cure-

At the other end of the table, Drusilla is STARING at the
tarot cards. Glances up at SPIKE ABOUT TO POUND DALTON.

                         DRUSILLA
                    Don't-

                         SPIKE
                    Why not? Some people find pain-

He SLAMS Dalton in the GUT, doubling him over.

                         SPIKE (cont'd)
                    -very inspirational.

Spike gets ready to punch him again. But Drusilla speaks up-

                         DRUSILLA
                    He can't help you.
                         (then)
                    Not without the key.

This stops Spike cold. He turns to her.

                         SPIKE
                    The key? You mean the book is in
                    some kind of code?

Drusilla nods. Spike drops Dalton in a heap - moves to her.
She nods to A TAROT CARD she has turned. Spike follows her
gaze.

CLOSE ON CARD

It is an etching of a ruined CRYPT, which is overgrown with
ivy - prominent above a field of tilted gravestones.

ON DRU AND SPIKE

                         SPIKE (cont'd)
                    Is that where we'll find this key?

Dru nods again. Spike grins.

                         SPIKE (cont'd)
                    I'll send the boys pronto.

                         DRUSILLA
                    Now will you dance?

                                                   CONTINUED

                              SPIKE
                    I'll dance with you, pet. On the
                    slayer's grave...

He laughs, lifts her gently into his arms - supporting her
frail body as he spins her to the music only she can hear.

                                        BLACK OUT.

                         END TEASER

ACT ONE

3 EXT. CEMETARY - NIGHT   3

Dead leaves scrape and tumble across the ground, riding a
stiff wind. A storm threatens. Under this we hear a
rhythmic TINK TINK TINK. We drift among the gravestones,
landing on Buffy in a close up. She is craning to hear the
sound. She turns, camera racking past her to a LARGE
MAUSOLEUM - one that matches THE PICTURE ON DRUSILLA's TAROT
CARD. Buffy moves toward it.

MOVING WITH BUFFY

The tinking sound grows louder as she nears the mausoleum.
She finds the solid iron door ajar. Torchlight flickers
hellishly through the narrow margin. Buffy looks inside.

WHAT SHE SEES

4 INT. MAUSOLEUM - NIGHT   4

A torch is set in the ground, illuminating the work of a dark
figure - who FINALLY BREAKS the lock of a vault door embedded
in the far wall. The thief opens the vault adn GRABS
something from it - then he makes for the exit.

5 EXT. CEMETARY - CONTINUOUS - NIGHT   5

Buffy waits for the thief to hit the exit. Then-

                    BUFFY
          Does "rest in peace" have no sanctity
          to you people?

She TACKLES HIM. The thief hits the ground hard and a red
velvet BAG that obviously contains something heavy falls from
his hands. We see now that it's DALTON - the vamp
transcriber.

                    BUFFY (cont'd)
          Oh, I forgot - you're not a people.

Buffy pulls a stake, is about to dust Dalton when ANOTHER
VAMPIRE appears behind her. He's formidable-looking. He
advances, unseen by Buffy...

Or so we think - until she wheels, knocking him back with a
vicious JUMPING KICK.

                                                        CONTINUED

5 CONTINUED: 5

Buffy grabs Vamp #1, drives him HEAD FIRST into a TREE TRUNK.   *
He crumples to the ground. She stakes him - dusto.

                    BUFFY (cont'd)
          One down-

Then she spins - ready to take on DALTON. But he's history.
And so is the red velvet bag he stole from the vault. On
Buffy's curiosity,

                    BUFFY (cont'd)
          One gone...

6 INT. BUFFY'S BEDROOM - NIGHT   6

ANGEL waits for Buffy. He wanders restlessly, looking at her
stuff. He does not notice as BUFFY appears at the open
window.

A beat as she watches him, oblivious to her. Then she TOSSES
her equipment bag into the room. Angel JUMPS - turns to
her - holding one of her stuffed animals. A CUTE PIG.

                    ANGEL
          Buffy - you scared me.

She climbs inside.

                    BUFFY
          Now you know what it feels like,
          stealth-guy.

She smiles, but the edge she had earlier is still evident.

                    BUFFY (cont'd)
          So. Just dropping by for some
          quality time with Mr. Gordo?

                    ANGEL
          Excuse me?

                    BUFFY
          The pig.

Angel looks down. Sees he's still holding the stuffed toy.

                    ANGEL
          Oh, I, no-

He puts the toy down - feeling dorky.

                                                            CONTINUED

6 CONTINUED: 6

                              BUFFY
                    What's up?

                              ANGEL
                    Nothing.

                              BUFFY
                    You don't have "nothing" face. You
                    have "something" face. And you don't
                    have to whisper. Mom's in L.A. till
                    Thursday. Art buying, or something.

                              ANGEL   *
                    Then why'd you come in through the   *
                    window?   *

                              BUFFY   *
                         (realizes)   *
                    Oh. Uh, habit. So, what's up?   *

                              ANGEL
                         (confesses)
                    I wanted to make sure you were okay.
                    I had a bad feeling.

                              BUFFY
                         (curt)
                    Oh surprise. Angel comes with bad
                    news.

          Angel reacts to her snipe. Buffy relents.

                              BUFFY (cont'd)
                    Sorry... I've been cranky miss all
                    day. It's not you.

                              ANGEL
                    What is it, then?

                              BUFFY
                    Nothing, its... We're having this   *
                    thing at school --

                              ANGEL
                    Career week?

                              BUFFY
                    How did you know?

                              ANGEL
                    I lurk.

                                                     CONTINUED

6 CONTINUED: (2)   6

                          BUFFY
               Oh, right. So you know, then. It's
               this whole week of "what's my line?"
               Only I don't get to play.
                    (then)
               Sometimes I just want...

She stops herself.

                                                      CONTINUED

6 CONTINUED: (2)   6

                    ANGEL
          You want - what? It's okay.

                    BUFFY
          The Cliffnotes version? I want a
          normal life. Like I had before.

                    ANGEL
          Before me.

A long beat. Buffy regards herself in her mirror. Alone.
Angel, of course, does not reflect. Finally-

                    BUFFY
          It's not that. It's just... This
          career business has me contemplating
          the el weirdo that I am. Let's face
          it - instead of a job I have a
          calling. Okay? No chess club or
          football games for me. I spend my
          free time in grave yards and dark
          alleys...

                    ANGEL
          Is that what you want? Football
          games?

                    BUFFY
          Maybe. Maybe not. But, you know
          what? - I'm never going to get the
          chance to find out. I'm stuck in
          this deal.

Angel reacts - can't hide his hurt. Moves to go.

                    ANGEL
          I don't want you to feel stuck-

Buffy realizes how she sounded. Stops him.

                    BUFFY
          Angel - I don't mean you. You're the
          one freaky thing in my freaky world
          that makes sense to me.
               (then)
          I just get messed sometimes - wish we
          could be like regular kids.

He nods, relenting.

                    ANGEL
          I'll never be a kid.

CONTINUED

6 CONTINUED: (4)   6

                         BUFFY
               Okay then. Just a regular kid and
               her 200 year-old, creature-of-the-   *
               night boyfriend.

Angel's eyes travel to the mirror - he notices something.

                         ANGEL
               Was this part of your normal life?

He reaches past her, plucks a photo from the mirror's frame.

INSERT PHOTO

A younger Buffy figure skating. Performing a perfect
arabesque.

RETURN

Buffy softens, takes the photo from him.

                         BUFFY
               My Dorothy Hamill phase. My room in
               L.A. was this major shrine -- Dorothy
               posters, Dorothy dolls. I even got
               the Dorothy haircut.
                    (embarrassed)
               Thereby securing a place for myself
               in the Geek Hall of Fame.

                         ANGEL
               You wanted to be like her.

                         BUFFY
               I wanted to be her.
                    (then)
               My parents used to fight a lot.
               Skating was an escape. I felt safe...

Angel replaces the photograph in the mirror frame.

                         ANGEL
               When was the last time you put on
               your skates?

Buffy thinks.

                         BUFFY
               Like, a couple hundred demons ago.

                                                  CONTINUED

6 CONTINUED: (5)   6

                    ANGEL
          There's a rink out past Route 17.
          It's closed on Tuesdays.

                    BUFFY
          Tomorrow's Tuesday.

                    ANGEL
          I know.

     Off the charged look between them.   *

7 EXT. PALM COURT - DAY   7

     Between-period mayhem. Xander and Cordelia stand in front of *
     a large sign that lists the results of the aptitude tests -   *
     each looking for their assignments.   *

                    CORDELIA   *
          Here I am. Personal shopper or   *
          Motivational speaker. Neato!   *

                    XANDER   *
          Motivational speaker? On what?   *
          "Ten steps to a more annoying you?"   *

                    CORDELIA   *
          Oh. And what about you? You're -   *

     She looks at the test results - finds his name. And starts   *
     to laugh. She moves off and Xander looks desperately at the   *
     sign.   *

                    XANDER   *
          What? What?   *

     ON BUFFY AND WILLOW   *

     Who walk nearby.   *

                    WILLOW
          You and Angel are going skating?   *
          Alone?

                    BUFFY
          Unless some unforeseen evil pops up.
          But I'm in full see-no-evil mode.

                                                         CONTINUED

7 CONTINUED: 7

                        WILLOW
          Angel, ice-skating...

                        BUFFY
          I know. Two worlds collide.

Xander catches up to them. Severely disturbed.

                        XANDER
          Wouldn't you two say you know me
          about as well as anyone? Maybe even
          better than I know myself?

                        WILLOW
          What's this about?

CONTINUED

                    XANDER
              (point blank)
     When you look at me, do you think
     prison guard?

Buffy and Willow look him over appraisingly.

                    BUFFY
     Crossing guard, maybe. But prison
     guard?

She shakes her head.

                    XANDER
     They just put up the assignments for
     the career fair. And according to my
     test results, I can look forward to
     being gainfully employed in the
     growing field of corrections.

                    BUFFY
     At least you'll be on the right side
     of the bars.

                    XANDER
     Laugh now, missy. They assigned you
     to the booth for 'law enforcement
     professionals.'

                    BUFFY
     As in police?

                    XANDER
     As in polyester, donuts, and
     brutality.

                    BUFFY
     Uggh.

                    WILLOW
              (cheerfully)
     But... donuts...

Buffy doesn't love this news, when something O.C. draws her
attention.

                    BUFFY
     I'll jump off that bridge when I come
     to it. First I have to deal with
     Giles --

                                              CONTINUED

7 CONTINUED: (2)   7

GILES is entering the school up ahead, a foot-tall stack of   *
books teetering under his chin.

                    BUFFY (cont'd)
          He's on this Tony Robbins hyper-
          efficiency kick. He wants me to
          check in with him now every day after
          homeroom.

She moves off. Willow turns to Xander:

                    WILLOW
          You didn't check to see which seminar
          I was assigned to, did you?

                    XANDER
          I did. And you weren't.

                    WILLOW
          I wasn't what?

                    XANDER
          On any of the lists.

Willow is confused.

                    WILLOW
          But I handed in my test. I used a
          number two pencil.

                    XANDER
          Then I guess you must've passed.

                    WILLOW
          It's not the kind of test you pass or
          fail.

                    XANDER
          Your name wasn't up there, Will.

Off Willow, who wonders why she's not on the list --

8 INT. LIBRARY - DAY   8

Giles struggles, trying to set the books down on a library
table. They tilt, about to topple - when Buffy catches them.

                    GILES
          Oh, Buffy. Thank you.

She helps ease them down for a safe landing.

                                                          CONTINUED

8 CONTINUED: 8

                         GILES (cont'd)
          I've been indexing the Watcher
          Diaries covering the past two
          centuries. You'd be amazed at how   *
          pompous and long-winded some of these
          watchers were.

                         BUFFY
          Color me stunned.

Giles opens his notebook.

                         GILES
          I trust last night's patrol was
          fruitful.

                         BUFFY
          Semi. I caught one out of two vamps
          after they stole something from this
          jumbo mausoleum at the cemetery-

                         GILES
          They were stealing?

                         BUFFY
          Yep. They had tools and the whole
          nine yards...
                    (then)
          What does that mean? The whole nine
          yards... nine yards of what? Now
          that's gonna bug me all day.

When Buffy comes out of her thought bubble, she sees Giles
pacing, visibly disturbed.

                         BUFFY (cont'd)
          Giles, you're in pace mode. What
          gives?

                         GILES
          The vampire who escaped - did you see
          what he took?

                         BUFFY
          No - but let me take a wild guess.
          Some old thing?

                         GILES
          I'm serious, Buffy.

                                                      CONTINUED

8 CONTINUED: (2)   8

                          BUFFY
                So am I. I bet it was downright
                crusty.

        Giles is losing patience with her.

                          GILES
                So you made no effort to find out
                what was taken?

        Buffy looks at Giles, surprised by his tone.

                          BUFFY
                Have a cow, Giles. I thought it was
                just everyday vamp hijinks.

                          GILES
                Well it wasn't. It could be very
                serious. If you'd made more of an
                effort to be thorough in your
                observations-

                          BUFFY
                     (cutting him off/hurt)
                If you don't like the way I'm doing
                my job - why don't you find someone
                else? Oh right. "There can be only
                one." Long as I'm alive, there isn't
                anyone else. Well, there you go! I
                don't have to be the Slayer. I could
                be dead!

                          GILES
                That's not terribly funny. You'll
                notice I don't laugh.

                          BUFFY
                Death wouldn't be much of a change,
                anyway. I mean, either way I'm
                bored, constricted, I never get to
                shop and my hair and fingernails
                continue to grow so really, what's
                the dif?

                          GILES
                Must we be introspective now? Our
                only concern at this moment should be
                to discover what was stolen from that
                mausoleum last night.

                                           CUT TO:

                                                            *

9 A LARGE SILVER CRUCIFIX   9

atop a velvet pillow. The cross bar is dotted with what
appear to be randomly placed HOLES, like swiss cheese.

                    SPIKE (O.S.)
               This is it, then?

WIDEN AND WE ARE:

10 INT. FACTORY - DRUSILLA'S BEDROOM - DAY   10

Spike sits at the edge of her bed, holding the pillowed cross
out to Drusilla like an offering. Drusilla's quivering hands
hover over the crucifix, but don't make contact. As if she's
warming them.

                    DRUSILLA
               It hums. I can hear it.

                    SPIKE
               Once you're well again, we'll have a
               coronation down main street. We'll
               invite everyone... and drink for
               seven days and seven nights-

                    DALTON (O.S.)
               What about the Slayer?

ANGLE TO INCLUDE DALTON

Standing at a deferential distance. Spike turns, angry at
the interruption.

                    DALTON
               She almost blew the whole thing for
               us. She's trouble.

                    SPIKE
                    (sarcastic)
               You don't say...

Now Spike is pacing again, ramping up with every word.

                    SPIKE (cont'd)
               Trouble? She's the gnat in my ear.
               The gristle in my teeth. The bloody
               thorn in my bloody side!

He slams the table with his fist - alarming even Dru.

                    DRUSILLA
               Spike-

                                                      CONTINUED

10   CONTINUED: 10

                         SPIKE
               No. Smart guy is right. We have to
               do something. There's no way we'll
               complete your cure with that bitch
               breathing down our necks...
                         (then/realizing)
               I need the big guns. They'll take
               care of her. Once and for all.

                         DALTON
               Big guns?

                         SPIKE
               The Order of Taraka.   *

     Dalton is clearly taken aback by the name.

                         DALTON
               The bounty hunters? For the Slayer?

     Dru takes her DECK OF TAROT CARDS from the bedside. Peels
     three from the deck - gazes at them.

                         DRUSILLA
               They're coming to my party, three of
               them.

                         DALTON
               But... The Order of Taraka. I mean,   *
               don't you think that's overkill?

     Spike grins. Looks down at Drusilla's cards.

                         SPIKE
               No. I think it's just enough kill.

     Camera follows his look down to the cards -- where three
     images have formed. Ominous, archetypal etchings of a
     CYCLOPS, a WORM, and a JAGUAR. Creeping in on the fearsome
     triumvirate, we:

                                             BLACK OUT.

                         END OF ACT ONE

ACT TWO

11 INT. SCHOOL LOUNGE - DAY   11

A WALL CLOCK

reads 2:30. We hear the frenetic buzz of activity.

The career fair is up and running. Students cluster around
a dozen or more booths manned by representatives from various
professions. Among them, a PHYSICIAN, a U.S. POSTAL WORKER,
and a UNIFORMED POLICEWOMAN. CAMERA drifts through the
thickening crowd... finds Willow worriedly surveying the
action. Xander steps up to her.

                    XANDER
          What are you doing here? Fly! Be
          free little bird - you defy category!

                    WILLOW
          I'm looking for Buffy.

                    XANDER
          She left with Giles an hour ago.
          Some kind of - "field trip" - deal.

                    WILLOW
          If she doesn't get back soon,
          Snyder's really --
                    (suddenly perking up)
          -- done a fantastic job setting up
          the fair this year, hasn't he,
          Xander?

SNYDER has marched up to them.

                    XANDER
                    (facetious)
          Principal Snyder! Great career fair,
          sir. Really. In fact, I'm so
          inspired by your leadership - I'm
          thinking principal school. I want to
          walk in your shoes. Not your actual
          shoes, of course. Because you're a
          tiny person. Not tiny in the small
          sense, of course...
                    (then)
          Okay. Done now.

Snyder doesn't even grace this with response.

                                        CONTINUED

                    SNYDER
               (to Willow)
          Where is she?

                    WILLOW
               (innocently)
          Who?

                    SNYDER
          You know who.

                    WILLOW
          Oh, you mean Buffy? I just saw her-

                    SNYDER
          And don't feed me that I-just-saw-her-
          a-minute-ago-she's-around-here-
          somewhere story.

Willow is like a deer caught in headlights.

                    WILLOW
          But I did - see her a minute ago.
          And she is - around here somewhere.

                    XANDER
          For what it's worth-

                    SNYDER
          It's worth nothing, Harris. Whatever
          sound comes out of your mouth is a
          meaningless waste of breath. An
          airborne toxic event.

                    XANDER
          I'm glad you feel comfortable enough
          to be so honest with me. And I only
          hope I'm in a position one day to be
          an honest with you.

Snyder looks at Xander as if examining a rare bug.

                    SNYDER
          Fascinating.

He moves off-

                    XANDER
          I'd love to stay and chat, but I have
          an appointment with the warden on
          standard riot procedure.

                         WILLOW
          Okay. See you-

Xander moves off. Willow gives him a slightly forlorn little
wave.

                         SUIT MAN
          Willow Rosenberg.

She turns-

ANGLE TO INCLUDE TWO SECRET SERVICE-TYPE MEN

Flanking Willow - not threateningly, but commandingly. They
wear identical dark suits.

                         SUIT MAN (cont'd)
          Come with us please?

                         WILLOW
          Excuse me?

                         SUIT MAN
          Let's walk.

Willow reluctantly allows herself to be led past several
booths... To a velvet cordon, stepping up into:

12 THE ELEVATED SECTION OF THE LOUNGE   12

Two free-standing walls separate this area from the general
population -- and Willow feels like she's dropped down the
rabbit hole. The space has been refurbished into a deco
salon. Soft lighting. A gentle BOSSA NOVA plays from hidden
speakers. On the wall there is a LOGO of a company that
looks STRANGELY LIKE the MICROSOFT LOGO.

A white-gloved WAITER approaches with a sliver tray of hors
d'oevres.

                         SUIT MAN
          Try the canape. It's excellent.

                         WILLOW
          What is all this?

                                                      CONTINUED

12 CONTINUED: 12

                         SUIT MAN
              You've been selected to meet with Mr.
              McCarthy, head recruiter for the
              world's leading software concern.
              The jet was delayed by fog at Sea-
              Tac, but he should be here any minute-
                         (then)
              Please. Make yourself comfortable.   *

He and suit guy #2 start to leave, but Willow stops them.

                         WILLOW
              But - I didn't even get my test back.

                         SUIT MAN
              The test was irrelevant. We've been
              tracking you for some time.

                         WILLOW
              Is that I good thing?

                         SUIT MAN
              I would think so. We're extremely
              selective. In fact, only one other
              Sunnydale student met our criteria.

Now Suit Man and his cohort exit through the partition.
Willow takes in her surroundings, stunned.

She turns - sees, for the first time, that OZ IS THE OTHER
STUDENT SUIT MAN was referring to. He's sitting on a plush
couch, looking unfazed - as usual. When he sees Willow, his
expression registers the coolest hint of delight.

Willow moves to the couch - sits next to him. An awkward
beat. This whole thing is too strange. Finally, OZ lifts
the hors d'oevres. Offers one to Willow.

                         OZ
              Canape?

13 EXT. CEMETARY - DAY - MOVING   13

Giles tries to keep pace with Buffy, who moves at a brisk
clip, still hurt from before. She carries a flashlight.

                         GILES
              Buffy. Please. Slow down...

                                                          CONTINUED

13 CONTINUED: 13

                    BUFFY
          Get with the program, Giles. We have
          work to do, remember?

                    GILES
          You're behaving in a terribly
          immature manner-

                    BUFFY
          Bingo. Know why? I am immature!
          I'm a teen! I've yet to mature!

                    GILES
          I was simply offering a little
          constructive criticism-

                    BUFFY
          You were harsh. You act like I
          picked this gig. But I'm the picked.
          Too bad if I want a normal job.

                    GILES
          What you have is more than a... gig.
          It's a sacred duty.

Buffy gives him a "been there, heard that" look. Giles
scrambles - trying to calm her.

                    GILES (cont'd)
          Which shouldn't prevent you from
          eventually procuring a more...
          mundane form of employment if you
          like. Such as I have.

                    BUFFY
          It's one thing being a Watcher and a
          librarian. They go together - like
          chicken and... another chicken. Two
          chickens. Or something.

Off Giles' look.

                    BUFFY (cont'd)
          You know what I'm saying - you can
          spend all your time with a bunch of
          books and no one blinks. But what
          can I do? Carve stakes for a nursery?

                    GILES
          Point taken... I suppose I've never
          really thought about-
                    (more)

13 CONTINUED: (2)   13

                         GILES (cont'd)
                      (sudden great idea)   *
             I say -- have you ever considered law   *
             enforcement?

Buffy blinks. Though she's spared from having to answer
because they've come to the mausoleum.

                         BUFFY
             This is the place.

Buffy pulls open the heavy iron door, enters, Giles following
her into:

14 INT. MAUSOLEUM - DAY   14

Buffy snicks on her flashlight, guiding the beam through the
dusty gloom. She leads Giles to the open vault door.

                         GILES
             May I?

                         BUFFY
             Be my guest.

Giles takes the flashlight. Shines it into the empty vault.

                         GILES
             It's a reliquary, used to house items
             of religious significance. Most
             commonly, a finger or some other body
             part from a saint.

                         BUFFY
             Note to self: Religion - freaky.

Giles turns, paints the wall with the flashlight beam --
which now falls across letters carved in the granite above
the doorway: du Lac.

                         GILES
             du Lac...
                      (with recognition and
                       concern)
             Oh dear.

Buffy reacts to his tone.

                         BUFFY
             I hate when you say that.

                                                          CONTINUED

14 CONTINUED: 14

                         GILES
          Josephus du Lac is buried here.

                         BUFFY
          Was he a saint?

                         GILES
          Hardly. He belonged to a sect of
          priests who were excommunicated by
          the Vatican at the turn of the
          century.

                         BUFFY
          Excommunicated and sent to Sunnydale.
          Must have been big with the sinning.

                         GILES
          Remember the book that was stolen
          from the library by a vampire a few
          weeks back? It was written by Du lac
          and his cohorts-
                    (frustrated)
          Damn it. In all the excitement, I
          let it slip my mind-

                         BUFFY
          I'm guessing it wasn't a Taste of the
          Vatican Cookbook.

                         GILES
          The book is said to contain rituals
          and spells that reap unspeakable
          evil. However, it was written in
          archaic latin - so nobody but the
          sect members could read it.

A15 EXT. CEMETERY - CONTINUOUS - DAY   A15   *

                         BUFFY
          Then everything's cool. The sect is
          gone. Worm food like old du Lac,
          right?

                         GILES
          I don't like it, Buffy. First the
          book is taken from the library. Now
          vampires steal something from du
          Lac's tomb...

                                                      CONTINUED

A15 CONTINUED: A15

                           BUFFY
                You think they've figured out how to
                read the book?

                                              CONTINUED

14 CONTINUED: (2)   14

                          GILES
          I don't know. But something's
          coming, Buffy. And I guarantee,
          whatever it is - it's not good.

With which Giles moves off purposefully, Buffy following.
Hold on the black interior of the vault-

15 EXT. BUS STATION - DAY   15

The sign on the brick wall reads: SUNNYDALE. A BUS rumbles
into frame, squeals to a stop in a cloud of exhaust.

CLOSE ON THE STAIRS OF THE BUS

We hear the doors open with a hydraulic hiss. A passenger
gets off. And another. Then an ENORMOUS PAIR OF BOOTS fill
the frame.

We pan up to see a GIANT. Seven feet tall in boots, and a
hard four hundred pounds. A thick, milky cataract covers one
eye. His other eye is set deep in the fleshy mask of
assorted scars and carbuncles he calls a face. His name is
OCTARUS. And as he descends the stairs and moves out of
frame-

                                          CUT TO:

16 EXT. NEIGHBORHOOD - DAY   16

A mild-mannered man in a suit too large for his slight frame
strides down the sidewalk, toting a brief case and whistling.
His name is MR. PFISTER. He moves past a familiar house -
past the sidewalk mail box on which is stencilled the name
"SUMMERS." He moves up the walk of the ADJACENT house.

ANOTHER ANGLE

Mr. Pfister climbs the stoop, and rings the doorbell. He
mechanically adjusts the knot in his tie. He smiles at the
tired-looking HOUSEWIFE who opens the door.

                      MR. PFISTER
          Mrs. Kalish?

                      MRS. KALISH
          Yes?

                                                    CONTINUED

16 CONTINUED: 16

                          MR. PFISTER   *
            I'm Norman Pfister, with Blush
            Beautiful Skin Care. I'm not selling   *
            anything, so I'm not asking you to
            buy.
                    (holds up case)
            Just to accept a few free samples.

                          MRS. KALISH
            Free?

                          MR. PFISTER
            Absolutely.

She considers him for a moment, then opens the door for him.
He enters past her, and she closes the door.

Hold for a beat. Another beat. Then an ear-splitting SCREAM
issues from behind the closed door. Prelap the thundering
sound of four JET ENGINES, as:

                                                    CUT TO:

17 EXT. AIRPORT - DAY (STOCK)   17

    A 767 comes in for a landing.

18 INT. 767 CARGO HOLD - DAY   18

    Dark. Jet engines rev down. We hear METALLICA bleeding up.
    KA-CHUNK. The hatch opens. Sunlight blasts inside. Along
    with the heavy metal. A BAGGAGE HANDLER climbs into the
    hold, his Walkman cranked up past eleven.

19 CREEPING POV   19

    Someone - or something - observes the handler from behind the
    cargo netting. As he begins downloading luggage onto the
    conveyor belt.

    ANGLE: HANDLERS

    The baggage handler pauses to air guitar a solo, when he sees
    a SILHOUETTE dart between crates, then melt into the shadows.

                          BAGGAGE HANDLER
            What the hell -

    He kills the tape, starts toward the shadows.

                                                    CONTINUED

19 CONTINUED: 19

                    BAGGAGE HANDLER (cont'd)
            Hey! You're not supposed to be in
            here...

But there's no answer.

                    BAGGAGE HANDLER (cont'd)
            Come on-

His thought is CUT SHORT by a series of BLOWS which come out
of nowhere, rocks him back on his heels. He falls to the
floor, moaning slightly so we know he's not dead.

FOOTSTEPS echo. A shadow stretches across the fallen
handler. Camera tracks slowly along the lengthening shadow
to the open hatch, where the silhouetted figure now stands.

We stop on an ETHNIC YOUNG WOMAN (17), her feline, feral eyes
getting used to the sudden light. She's a predator, a
hunter, and her name is KENDRA. And as she jumps out of
frame, onto the tarmac-

                                            CUT TO:

20 EXT. SUNNYDALE HIGH - LATE DAY (STOCK)   20

Pretty much dead. Sports practices and extra-curricular
activities are done for the day. Except-

21 INT. LIBRARY   21

Buffy, Willow, and Xander sit around the table.

                    WILLOW
                (to Buffy)
            So Giles is sure that the vampire who
            stole his book is connected to the
            one you slayed last night? Or is it
            "slew?"

                    GILES (O.S.)
            Both are correct.

Giles emerges from the stacks with a yellowed periodical.

                    GILES
            And yes. I'm sure.

Giles sets the magazine down before them. It's a National
Geographic, circa 1921.

CONTINUED

21   CONTINUED: 21

                         GILES (cont'd)
          du Lac was both a theologian and a
          mathematician. This article
          describes an invention of his, which
          he called The du Lac Cross-

                         XANDER
          Why go to all the trouble of
          inventing something and then give a
          weak name like that? I'd have gone
          with "Cross-o-matic!" or "The Amazing
          Mr. Cross!.."

Xander is getting the stare again. He stops. Then Giles
indicates a yellowing photo of the stolen crucifix. Willow
peruses the accompanying article.

                         GILES
          The cross was more than a symbol. It
          was also used to understand certain
          mystical texts -- to decipher hidden
          meanings and so forth.

                         BUFFY
          You're saying these vampires went to
          all that trouble for your basic
          decoder ring?

Giles regards her for a blank beat. Then:

                         GILES
          Actually, I guess I am.

                         WILLOW
                (re: article)
          According to this, du Lac destroyed
          every one of the crosses - except the
          one buried with him.

                         BUFFY
          Why destroy his own work?

                         GILES
          I suppose he feared what might happen
          if the cross fell into the wrong
          hands.

                         XANDER
          A fear we'll soon get to experience
          for ourselves, up close and personal.

CONTINUED

                         GILES
          Unless we preempt their plans-

                         WILLOW
          How?

                         GILES
          By learning what was in the book
          before they do.

Giles regards the group with grim purpose.

                         GILES (cont'd)
          Which means we can expect to be here
          late tonight-

                         WILLOW
          Goody! Research party!

                         XANDER
          Will, you need a life in the worst
          way-

                         BUFFY
          Speaking of... I have to bail... I
          promise I'll be back bright and
          early, perky and ready to slay.

Giles looks at her, perplexed.

                         GILES
          This is a matter of some urgency,
          Buffy.

                         BUFFY
          I know. But you have to admit, I
          lack in the book area. You guys are
          the brains. I'd just be around for
          moral support-

                         XANDER
          That's not true, Buffy. You totally
          contribute. You go for snacks.

Willow and Buffy exchange a quick glance. Will knows what's
up.

                         WILLOW
          She should go. You know, gather her
          strength?

                                              CONTINUED

21 CONTINUED: (3)   21

                    GILES
          Perhaps you're right. There may be
          fierce battles ahead.

                    XANDER
          But - Ho Ho's are a vital part of my
          cognitive process...

                    BUFFY
          Sorry, Xand. I have something I
          really need to do tonight-

Off Giles and Xander's curious faces.

22 INT. SKATING RINK - NIGHT   22

CLOSE ON

A PAIR OF ICE SKATES as they SHAVE THE ICE, stopping on a
dime.

WIDEN TO INCLUDE BUFFY

Alone on the ice, which seems to glow from the moonlight
filtering in from the high-grimy windows.

She breathes in the cool air - takes off again.

MOVING WITH BUFFY

as she enters a clear frame, picking up speed. Remembering
the movement. And the rush. Her blowing hair frames a smile
she hasn't allowed herself in the longest time.

ANGLE - POV FROM BLEACHERS

Watching Buffy skate. Spinning into a tight pirouette.
She's good. She's very good.

REVERSE ANGLE

The darkness seems to shift - as a face distinguishes itself
from the shadows. Watching Buffy. It's Octarus. The HUGE,
SCARY GUY. As we-

                                        BLACK OUT.

                    END OF ACT TWO

ACT THREE

23   INT. SKATING RINK - NIGHT   23

GLIDING LOW AND FAST

With Buffy's skates across the ice, then tilting up to Buffy.
She's transported, her face set in a concentrated smile.

She pivots, skating backward, getting up her nerve and
picking up speed - then launching into an airborne twirl-

Losing her balance at the apex, and-

LOW ANGLE

Buffy lands hard, the momentum carrying her a good ten feet
before she comes to a stop.

She catches her breath - when she sees a shadow move across
the ice in front of her. She looks around hopefully-

                    BUFFY
          Angel?

Only it's not Angel. It's OCTARUS. And his giant hands are
already AROUND HER NECK. He lifts her like a rag doll and
carries her OFF THE ICE AND ONTO THE RINK'S RUBBER DECK -
pinning her AGAINST THE WALL.

Buffy thrashes - pulls on Octarus' HUGE HANDS - but finds
herself unable to break his grip. He tightens his hold on
her and we see a horrible and unfamiliar fear on Buffy's
face - the fear of death.

                    ANGEL (O.C.)
          Buffy!

Octarus' turns at the interruption, just in time to meet
Angel's FIST. Octarus releases his grip on Buffy, and she
falls to the ground in a gasping heap.

REVEAL

ANGEL IN FULL VAMP FURY

AS OCTARUS slams a HAM SIZED FIST into his face - sending him
sprawling. Angel immediately gets up to defend himself, but
finds he is trapped in an alcove.

                                                    CONTINUED

23 CONTINUED: 23

Angel ROARS, standing his ground bravely as Octarus moves in
for the kill-

ANGLE: BUFFY

regains her feet. Seeing Angel in trouble, she vaults over
a wooden bench, and:

ANOTHER ANGLE

Buffy lands directly behind Octarus.

As he turns, she takes to the air, executing a textbook
SPINNING WHEEL KICK (SLIGHT OVERCRANK), leading with teh
GLISTENING BLADE of her ice skate. In the blur of contact,
we hear a sickening TEAR-

ON ANGEL

Even he grimaces at this one.

We TILT up to OCTARUS, as he clutches his throat. He looks
at Buffy, face full of betrayal - then starts toward her.
Buffy moves out of the way, her guard raised. But Octarus
moves past her, out onto the ice-

ANGLE: BUFFY

watches. Angel steps up behind her, vamp face still on.

THEIR POV

Octarus staggers like a drunken sailor, with pathetic
persistence - before collapsing onto his knees and doing a
face plant on the ice. Hold for an uncomfortable beat-

                                        CUT TO:

24 INT. FACTORY - DRUSILLA'S BEDROOM - NIGHT   24

CLOSE ON THE CYCLOPS CARD

Drusilla's pale fingers turn it over.

                    DRUSILLA (O.C.)
              He's passing under our feet... right
              now.

25 WIDER   25

     Spike is seated on the bed beside Drusilla. He notes the
     card with concern, then looks to Drusilla.

                         SPIKE
               No worries. We're close to decoding
               the manuscript. We just need a
               little more time.

                         DRUSILLA
               Time is ours-

     Drusilla touches Spike's face, smoothing away the worry.

                         DRUSILLA (cont'd)
               It brings the slayer closer to them.

     She eyes the remaining cards -- the WORM and the JAGUAR.   *

                                        CUT TO:

26 INT. SKATING RINK - NIGHT   26

     ANGEL: ON THE ICE

     Angel kneels beside the fallen behemoth. He still has his
     vamp face - and the blow he took OPENED A CUT ABOVE ONE EYE.   *
     Which Buffy can't see as she limps painfully up behind him.   *

                         BUFFY
               And the hellmouth presents - 'Dead
               Guys On Ice'. Not exactly the
               evening we were aiming for...

     Angel reacts to the CHUNKY RING on Octarus' finger. He lifts
     the giant's hand, studies the glyph-like pattern etched on
     the surface.

                         ANGEL
               You're in danger. You know what the
               ring means?

                         BUFFY
               I just killed a Superbowl Champ?

                         ANGEL
               I'm serious. You should go home and
               wait until you hear from me.

     Angel drops Octarus' hand and turns to her. Sees that she's
     injured.

                                                    CONTINUED

26   CONTINUED:

>   ANGEL (cont'd)
>   Are you okay?

>   BUFFY
>   What about you?   That cut-

>   ANGEL
>   Forget about me.   You're hurt.

Buffy's shaken - but she puts on her brave face.

>   BUFFY
>   Hey.   No biggy.   I've been slammed by
>   bigger sides of beef than that-

>   ANGEL
>   No you haven't.

Buffy falters.   He's right.

>   BUFFY
>   No.   I haven't.

>   ANGEL
>   This is bad, Buffy.   We have to get
>   you someplace safe.

Buffy is rightfully alarmed by the suggestion.

>   BUFFY
>   You mean - hide?

>   ANGEL
>   Let's just get you out of here.

He starts to move but Buffy stops him - indicates his bloody
cut.

>   BUFFY
>   Wait.   Your eye is all...   Let me-

She moves toward him - about to use the arm of her sweatshirt
to wipe the blood off.   But he pulls away.

>   BUFFY (cont'd)
>   Come on.   Don't be a baby.   I won't
>   hurt you.

CONTINUED

26 CONTINUED: (2)   26

                         ANGEL
              It's not that.
                    (re: vamp face)
              I - you shouldn't have to touch me
              when I'm like this.

Buffy is at a loss.

                         BUFFY
              Like - what?

Angel reacts - is she kidding?

                         ANGEL
              You know. When I'm...

                         BUFFY
              Oh.

A long beat as Buffy takes this in, understanding.

She approaches him again. Very deliberately this time. Her
hands go to his face. He looks away, but does not pull back.
The gentleness of her touch holds him fast.

Buffy turns his face back to hers. Tenderly runs her fingers
along his transformed features. Angel is overwhelmed.
Nobody has ever touched him like this.

                         BUFFY (cont'd)
              I didn't even notice.

She draws him close. Gaze steady. Until her lips touch
his...

They melt into a heart-stopping kiss.

27 INT. SKATING RINK - ANOTHER AREA - NIGHT   27

KENDRA, the LETHAL YOUNG WOMAN from the airport, peers
through some bleachers.

HER POV - HAND HELD PAN THROUGH BLEACHERS

THE KISS. Still very much a work in progress.

                                        FADE TO:

28 INT. LIBRARY - DAY   28

CLOSE ON

The ring OCTARUS' wore.

WIDEN TO INCLUDE GILES

Who studies the ring, comparing it to an etching in a book.
Buffy sits near by, AN ICE PACK on one knee, definitely
looking shaky and worse for the wear after her encounter with
OX GUY. Willow and Xander are also there.

                    BUFFY
          This guy was hard core, Giles. And
          Angel was power-freaked by the ring.

                    GILES
          I'm afraid he was not overreacting.
          The ring is worn only by members of
          The Order of Taraka. They are a
          society of demon assasains dating
          back to King Solomon...

                    XANDER
          And didn't they beat the Elks last
          year in the Sunnydale Adult Bowling
          League Championship?

                    GILES
               (ignoring him)
          Their credo is to sow discord and
          kill the unwary.

                    XANDER
          Bowling is a vicious game-

                    GILES
               (sharp)
          That's enough, Xander-

Willow, Xander and Buffy glance at each other, reacting to
Giles' tone. Buffy, especially, knows to worry.

                    GILES (cont'd)
          I'm sorry but this is no time for
          jokes. I need to think.

                    BUFFY
          These assassins... Why would they be
          after me?

                                                    CONTINUED

28 CONTINUED: 28

                         WILLOW
              'Cause you're the scourge of the
              underworld?

                         BUFFY
              Yeah, but I haven't been that scourgy
              lately.

                         GILES
              I don't know. But I think the best
              thing to do is to find a secure
              location. Someplace out of the way
              where you can go until we decide on
              the best course of action-

Buffy stands with a little difficulty. Officially freaked.

                         BUFFY
              Okay. You and Angel have both told
              me to head for the hills. What's the
              deal?

                         GILES
              I - this is an extraordinary
              circumstance...

                         BUFFY
                   (scared)   *
              You're saying I can't handle this?   *
              These guys are that bad?

                         GILES
              You might- They're... They're a
              breed apart, Buffy. Unlike
              vampires - they have no earthly
              desire except to collect their
              bounty. To find their target and
              eliminate it-

CAMERA pushes in slowly as Buffy listens to Giles' cautionary
litany-

                         GILES (cont'd)
              And you are the target. You can kill
              as many of them as you like.
                   (more)

                                                    CONTINUED

28 CONTINUED: (2)   28

                          GILES (cont'd)
                 It won't make any difference -
                 because where there is one, there
                 will be another. And another. They
                 won't stop coming until the job is
                 done...

                                             CUT TO:

29 INT. MRS. KALISH'S HOUSE - DAY   29

     Mr. Pfister whistles to himself as he sits on a chair parked
     before a second story window. He's looking through a PAIR OF
     BINOCULARS and has them aimed directly across the way - right
     into BUFFY'S BEDROOM.

                          GILES (OVER)
                 The worst of it is, they are masters
                 of deceit. Vampires are bound by the
                 night, but these predators can be
                 anywhere, any time. They can appear
                 as normal as the next person. Just
                 another face in the crowd. You might
                 not ever know when one of them is
                 near - not until the moment of your
                 death...

     Under this, CAMERA arms around and pushes past him...
     discovering MRS. KALISH on the floor. Or at least what's
     left of her.

     Because now she's little more than a desiccated corpse. A
     dozen worms crawl out of her nose and march along the floor,
     joining the trail which we follow... back to Mr. Pfister.
     The worms scamper up his leg and waist... up to his right
     arm, which IS FORMED ONLY UP TO THE WRIST. The nub seems to
     undulate, as --

     The teeming mass of worms (CGI) REFORMS INTO HIS HIS HAND --
     which now delicately picks up a steaming cup of tea. He
     sips, waiting patiently. Prelap a SHRIEKING BELL --

                                             CUT TO:

30 INT. SCHOOL HALLWAY - DAY   30

     BUFFY MOVES upstream through the Career Fair gauntlet,
     against the teeming mass of people.

                                             CONTINUED

30 CONTINUED: 30

She is walking stiffly - evidence of her battle with
Octarus - and is clearly wigging out. her eyes dart - see in
every passerby a potential threat.

HER POV

The faces - students, teachers - seem innocent. But are
they? Voices melt into an echoing white noise. She moves
past the POLICE WOMAN... A PAIR OF CORDETTES...

Suddenly - a guy in the crowd surges toward her - FAST.
Something's not right.

RESUME BUFFY

She GRABS THE GUY BY THE COLLAR. DRIVES HIM INTO THE WALL.
It's OZ.

                    BUFFY
          Try it!

                    OZ
          Try what?

A moment, then Buffy lets him go.

                    BUFFY
          Sorry.

                    OZ
          I'm still not clear on what I'm
          supposed to try.

Buffy looks around - people are staring.

                    BUFFY
          Nothing.

Buffy heads for the door. BOLTS without another word.

                    OZ
          A tense person.

31 INT. LIBRARY - NIGHT   31

Giles and Willow sit at the library table, poring over volume
upon volume.

                    WILLOW
          I wish there was more we could do.

CONTINUED

31 CONTINUED: 31

    Giles looks up, his eyes reflecting fatigue and concern.

                          GILES
                We're doing all we can. The only
                course of action is to decipher the
                contents of the stolen book-

                          WILLOW
                I've never seen Buffy like that. She
                just took off...

                          XANDER (O.S.)
                She didn't go home.

    Xander has entered the library.

                          XANDER
                I let the phone ring a few hundred
                times before I remembered her mom's
                out of town.

                          GILES
                Maybe Buffy unplugged the phone...

                          XANDER
                It's a statistical impossibility for
                a sixteen year old girl to unplug a
                telephone.

    Willow nods. That's true.

                          GILES
                Perhaps my words of caution were a
                bit too alarming-

                          XANDER
                    (no duh)
                You think?

                          WILLOW
                It's good that she took you
                seriously, Giles. I just wish we
                knew where she was...

                                        CUT TO:

32 EXT. BUFFY'S HOUSE - NIGHT   32

    Buffy moves along the sidewalk, still limping a little. She
    looks tired and cold - like she has been walking a long time.
    She stops and looks up at her house. The windows are dark.

                                        CONTINUED

32 CONTINUED: 32

A long beat. No place feels safe. Not even here. She moves
on.

33 INT. FOYER - ANGEL'S APARTMENT - NIGHT   33

Buffy arrives at Angel's door. Knocks.

                    BUFFY
          Angel?

No answer. She tries the door. It's locked.

34 INT. ANGEL'S APARTMENT - NIGHT   34

Dark. Then the lock is FORCED and Buffy opens the door,
spilling light from the hallway.

                    BUFFY
          Hey...

She clicks on a standing lamp. Looks around. She approaches
the unmade bed pushed up against the wall. Sits.

She flexes her tender knee. Massages it. Her exhaustion and
fear finally catching up with her.

She lies down. Curls up - small and alone in his bed. Turns
her head against his pillow.

She breathes him in. Shuts her eyes.

35 INT. SEEDY BAR (THE ALIBI ROOM) - NIGHT   35

This is the kind of bar where the lights are so low it's hard
to see your hand in front of your face. Which is a good
thing. Because you wouldn't want to get a good look at
either the surroundings or the patrons.

It's after hours. A solitary stooped figure gives the floor
a perfunctory once-over with a stiff broom. This is WILLY,
a shifty-eyed bottom-dweller. In addition to being the
bartender here, he's a small time hustler who moves in the
underworld of the vampires - despite the fact that he is not
a vamp himself.

A SHADOWED FIGURE appears in the doorway. Willy looks up,
annoyed.

                                              CONTINUED

                         WILLY
              We're closed. Can't you read the
              sign?

The FIGURE moves into the room and we see that it is ANGEL.
WILLY's demeanor changes. He's clearly afraid of Angel.
Doesn't want any trouble.

                         WILLY (cont'd)
              Oh. Hey, Angel. I didn't recognize
              you in the dark there.

Angel just looks at Willy.

                         WILLY (cont'd)
              What - what can I do for you tonight?

                         ANGEL
              I need some information.

                         WILLY
              Yeah? Man. That's too bad. Cause'
              I'm staying away from that whole
              scene. I'm living right, Angel.

                         ANGEL
              Sure you are, Willy. And I'm taking
              up sunbathing.

                         WILLY
              Come on, now. Don't be that way. I
              treat you vamps good. I don't hassle
              you. You don't hassle me. We all
              enjoy the patronage of this
              establishment. Everybody's happy...

Angel moves closer to Willy. Menacing. Willy's anxiety
increases.

                         ANGEL
              Who sent them?

                         WILLY
              Who sent - who?

Lightening fast - Angel's HAND is AROUND WILLY'S NECK.
Willy's broom goes clattering to the floor as his eyes go
wide with fear and he gasps desperately for breath.

                         ANGEL
              The Order of Taraka.

                                                    CONTINUED

35 CONTINUED: (2)   35

                         WILLY
              I tell you - I haven't been in the
              loop-

                         ANGEL
              Let's try again. The Order of
              Taraka. They're after the slayer-   *

                         WILLY
              Come on, man...

                         ANGEL
              Was it Spike?

Angel tightens his grip. LIFTS WILLY slightly off the
ground. Willy tries to choke out a negotiation.

                         WILLY
              Angel, hey... I - I got some fresh
              pig's blood in. Good stuff. My
              fence said the white cell count is-

Angel is now moments from squeezing the life out of this guy.

                         ANGEL
              You know... I'm a little rusty when
              it comes to killing humans. It could
              take a while.

Willy is wavering. Clearly - his options are limited.

                         WILLY
              Spike will draw and quarter me, man-

Angel lets up a little. Puts him back on the ground.

                         ANGEL
              I'll take care of Spike.

Willy caves.

                         WILLY
              You know he ordered those guys.
              Spike's sick of your girl getting in
              his way.

                         ANGEL
              Where can I find him?

This is more than Willy should give up and he knows it.

                                                    CONTINUED

35 CONTINUED: (3)   35

                         WILLY
               I tell you that, and I'm gonna need
               relocating expenses. It'll cost you-

          BAM! Angel SLAMS Willy into the WALL. Still holding him by
          the neck.

                         ANGEL
               It will cost <u>who</u>?

          Willy can barely speak.

                         WILLY
               Okay... Okay!..
                    (then)
               He and that freaky chick of his are-

          Angel is listening so intently - he doesn't notice the BROOM
          HANDLE FLYING TOWARD HIS HEAD.

          Angel is BLIND-SIDED across the temple by an UNSEEN ATTACKER.
          He hits the GROUND. HARD. Willy also falls to the floor in
          a heap.

          ON THE ATTACKER

          Standing over ANGEL with the broom handle. It's KENDRA

          Her whole stance and attitude radiate lethal power. Her
          voice rings with contempt-

                         KENDRA
               Where is she?

                                        BLACK OUT.

                         END OF ACT THREE

ACT FOUR

36   INT. SEEDY BAR (WILLY'S ALIBI ROOM) - NIGHT   36

Back to that lethal young thang. Angels looks up at her,
spits-

                    KENDRA
          The girl. Where is she?

                    ANGEL
          Even if I knew - I wouldn't tell you.

Kendra BREAKS THE BROOM HANDLE over her knee.

                    KENDRA
          Then die.

ANGEL ROLLS out of the strike zone just as she brings the
make-shift stake down towards his heart.

                                                                    *

He gets to his feet - but she is ON HIM AGAIN in a flash.

                                                                    *

WILLY makes tracks for the exit. Disappears.

37   INT. SEEDY BAR STORAGE ROOM - NIGHT   37

The storage area is basically A CAGE - much like the one in
the library - where the expensive liquor and such is locked.

Angel and Kendra CRASH into a BOX FULL OF LIQUOR BOTTLES,
which shatter everywhere. Angel grabs a BROKEN BOTTLE -- we   *
see he has changed into a VAMP -- fends Kendra off with it.   *
Kendra hesitates.

                                                CONTINUED

                         ANGEL
               Who are you?

Kendra backs out of the storage area. Cool but clearly wary.

                         ANGEL (cont'd)
               I won't hurt you if you tell me what
               I need to know.

Unexpectedly - Kendra smiles. Angel doesn't see the humor in
the situation.

                         ANGEL (cont'd)
               You think this is funny?

Kendra SLAMS AND BOLTS THE STURDY METAL GATE that closes the
storage area.

                         KENDRA
               I think it's funny now...

Angel reacts. Moves to the locked door.

                         KENDRA (cont'd)
               That girl. The one I saw you with
               before-

                         ANGEL
               You stay away from her.

                         KENDRA
               I'm afraid you are not in a position
               to threaten.

                         ANGEL
               When I get out of here I'll do more
               than threaten-

                         KENDRA
               Then I suggest you move quickly.

She glances at a ROW OF HIGH WINDOWS THAT RUN ALONG ONE WALL
OF THE STORAGE CAGE.

                         KENDRA (cont'd)
               Eastern exposure. The sun comes in
               a few hours.
                         (then)
               More than enough time for me to find
               your girlfriend.

She moves off. Angel can only watch - frustrated.

                                                    CONTINUED

37 CONTINUED: (2)   37

A beat. Then he strains against the door of the cage,
determined to open it.

                                                     FADE TO:

38 INT. GILES' OFFICE - LIBRARY - EARLY MORNING   38

Giles, bleary-eyed and rumpled from a sleepless night of
urgent study, talks on the phone while he pages through a
book.

                    GILES
          Xander? ... No, I still haven't
          heard from Buffy. I think you should
          go to her house and check on her...

Giles sees something in the book. Something important.

                    GILES (cont'd)
          Right away. I don't know... get
          Cordelia to drive you.

He hangs up. Rushes into-

39 INT. LIBRARY - CONTINUOUS - DAY   39

Giles moves to the table and we see WILLOW, who has fallen
asleep at the computer.

He moves to her, gently shakes her. Still, she wakes with a
start, cries out-

                    WILLOW
          Don't wake the tadpoles!

Giles is startled by her outburst.

                    GILES
          My Goodness. Are you alright?

                    WILLOW
          Giles? What are you doing here?

                    GILES
          You're in the library, Willow. You
          fell asleep.

                    WILLOW
          Oh... I...

                                                  CONTINUED

39 CONTINUED: 39

                         GILES
              Don't warn the tadpoles?

                         WILLOW
              I - I have frog fear.
                    (then)
              I'm sorry... I conked out-

                         GILES
              Please. You've gone quite beyond the
              call of duty. And, fortunately, I
              think I've finally found something-

                         WILLOW
              You did?

                         GILES
                    (re: book)
              I had to go back to the Lutheran
              Index. But I found a description of
              the missing du Lac Manuscript. It's
              a ritual, Willow. I haven't managed
              to decipher the exact details - but
              I believe the purpose is to restore
              a weak and sickly vampire to full
              health.

                         WILLOW
              A vampire like - Drusilla?

                         GILES
              Exactly.

                         WILLOW
              What does that have to do with the
              Order of Taraka? The assasins?

                         GILES
              I would imagine Spike called them
              here to get Buffy out of the way.
              I'm sure he wants nothing to come
              between him and his plans to revive
              his lady love.

                         WILLOW
              So this is good. We know what the
              deal is.

                         GILES
              I wish I could agree. But all we
              know is the goal of the ritual.
                    (more)

                                                    CONTINUED

39 CONTINUED: (2)   39

                         GILES (cont'd)
          We don't know where it will take
          place or when... We don't know what
          it entails-

                         WILLOW
          So this is bad.

                         GILES
          No. No. We just have more work to
          do.

     Giles tries to smile encouragingly.

                         WILLOW
          Then - why are you all pinched?

     Off Giles - his worry palpable.

40 INT. FACTORY - EARLY MORNING   40

     CLOSE ON

     The DU LAC manuscript

     As it is SLAMMED SHUT.

     Widen to reveal a TRIUMPHANT SPIKE, who is standing over
     DALTON - the vampire scholar. Dalton hands Spike a sheet of
     paper with the complete transcription on it.

                         SPIKE
          By George - I think he's got it.

     Spike sweeps over to Drusilla with paper in hand. Drusilla,
     looking ever more pale and consumptive, sits propped on a
     velvet couch, her tarot cards laid out on her lap.

                         SPIKE (cont'd)
          The key to your cure, ducks! The
          missing bloody link! It was-

     Drusilla stops him as she takes his hand - leads it to a
     tarot card.

                         DRUSILLA
          - right in front of us.

                                                          CONTINUED

40 CONTINUED: 40

CLOSE ON THE CARD

A beautiful image of AN ANGEL. But the angel is FALLING -
plummeting through the sky to an all but certain doom.

                    DRUSILLA (O.C.)
          - the whole time.

41 EXT. BUFFY'S HOUSE - EARLY MORNING   41

All is peaceful here as the neighborhood is just beginning to
awaken.

42 EXT./INT. BUFFY'S HOUSE - LIVING ROOM - EARLY MORNING   42   *

Well mostly peaceful. We can make out Cordelia and Xander on
the porch through the curtains. Cordelia's SHRILL voice
penetrates the tranquility.

                    CORDELIA (O.C.)
          I can't even believe you. You drag
          me out of bed for a ride? What am I,
          mass transportation?

Xander knocks on the door.   *

                    XANDER
          That's what a lot of the guys say.
          But it's just locker room talk. I
          never pay it any mind...

                    CORDELIA   *
          Great. So now I'm your taxi and your
          punching bag-

                    XANDER
          I like to think of you more as my
          witless foil - but have it your way.
                                                                    *

CONTINUED

42 CONTINUED: 42

                         XANDER (cont'd)
              Come on, Cordy. You can't be a
              member the Scooby Gang if you aren't
              willing to be inconvenienced now and
              then-

Xander climbs in a window.   *

                         CORDELIA
              Oh, right. Cause' I lie awake at
              night hoping you tweekos will be my
              best friends. And that my first
              husband will be a balding, demented
              homeless man-

Xander opens the door for her. She enters.   *

                         XANDER
              Buffy could be in trouble-

                         CORDELIA
              And, what, exactly, are you going to
              do about it if she is? If you hadn't
              noticed - you're the lameness. She's
              the superchick or whatever.

                         XANDER
              At least I'm lameness that cares.
              Which is more than you can say.
                   (then)
              I'm going to check upstairs.

He STOMPS off, leaving a POUTY Cordelia behind. She starts
to look around the living room when she is interrupted by a
crisp KNOCK on the front door.

She moves to the door, looks through the window in the door.

WHAT SHE SEES

MISTER PFISTER - AKA BUG MAN. Pfister tips his hat - holds
up the bag that reads BLUSH BEAUTIFUL SKIN CARE.   *

ON CORDELIA

That's all she needed to see. She opens the door.

                         MR. PFISTER
              Good day. I am Norman Pfister with
              Blush Beautiful Skin Care and
              Cosmetics.
                   (more)

                                                            CONTINUED

42 CONTINUED: (2)   42

                         MR. PFISTER (cont'd)
              I was wondering if I might interest
              you in some free samples?

                         CORDELIA
              Free?

43   EXT. BUFFY'S HOUSE - EARLY MORNING   43

      Cordelia hesitates. Then, just as before with MRS. KALISH,
      Cordelia opens the door for Mr. Pfister.

      In an eerie reprise of the earlier scene - he enters past
      her, and she closes the door. A long ominous beat...

44   INT. SEEDY BAR STORAGE ROOM - EARLY MORNING   44

      The first glow of morning light warms the WINDOWS, as ANGEL
      works desperately to tear the metal door from its hinges.

                                                                    *

45   INT. ANGEL'S APARTMENT - EARLY MORNING   45

      In contrast to the sun-washed storage room, Angel's apartment
      is a cool, dark tomb. A haven from the waking world.

CLOSE ON BUFFY

      Curled in Angel's bed - arms tightly wrapped around his
      pillow. She is, for the moment, safe in his phantom embrace.

      A sound. Something moves in the apartment. Loud enough to
      rouse Buffy from her dream. Her eyes flutter - then SNAP
      OPEN just in time for her to DODGE THE SHORT AXE that SLAMS
      into the pillow just inches from her neck.

      Buffy LEAPS from the bed - comes face to face with KENDRA.

                        BUFFY
            You must be number two-

      Kendra replies with a SWING OF THE AXE, which BUFFY LEAPS to
      avoid.

                        BUFFY (cont'd)
            Thanks for the wake-up. But I'll
            stick with my clock radio...

                                                       CONTINUED

45 CONTINUED: 45

Lethal young woman brings the AXE down again, but BUFFY
CATCHES her arm mid-flight.

To Buffy's distress - she can't wrench the AXE from Kendra.
They are locked in a dead-even struggle. Like an arm
wrestling match between perfect twins. A split second as
they meet eyes - a twinge of recognition...

Then Buffy takes advantage of the moment - SWEEPS Kendra's
legs out from under her. Kendra hits the ground hard, but
USES her LEGS to PIN BUFFY'S LEGS and bring her down too.

Now BUFFY and Kendra ROLL on the floor - the AXE still in
Kendra's grip. They keep TRADING the UPPER HAND. One moment
Buffy is on top - the next it seems Kendra will prevail.
They SMASH into Angel's table, his bookshelf, his dresser...

Buffy's getting fed up.

                    BUFFY (cont'd)
          Come on. Don't make me do the chick
          fight thing-

Kendra doesn't know what to make of the comment. Speaks
through her effort-

                    KENDRA
          Chick... fight?

                    BUFFY
          You know-

BUFFY VIOLENTLY JERKS Kendra by the HAIR - distracting her as
she DIGS HER NAILS INTO THE HAND THAT HOLDS THE AXE.

Kendra cries out - drops the AXE. Buffy grabs it and
STRADDLES Kendra, pinning her. Buffy draws the axe back -
the intent clear. Still, she can't resist-

                    BUFFY (cont'd)
          Cliched - but effective.

Buffy is about to bring the axe down - but Kendra stops her
with-

                    KENDRA
          Who are you?

                    BUFFY
          What do you mean who am I? You
          attacked me. Who the hell are you?

                                                      CONTINUED

45 CONTINUED: (2)   45

    Kendra glares at Buffy.   Proud and defiant-

                      KENDRA
               I am Kendra, the vampire slayer.

    A long beat.   Buffy takes this in.   Come again?

                                        BLACK OUT.

            <u>END OF PART ONE</u>

BUFFY THE VAMPIRE SLAYER

"What's My Line? - Part Two"

Written By

Marti Noxon

Directed By

David Semel

SHOOTING SCRIPT

October 15, 1997
October 17, 1997 (Blue Pages)
October 28, 1997 (Pink Pages)

BUFFY THE VAMPIRE SLAYER

"What's My Line? - Part Two"

CAST LIST

BUFFY SUMMERS......................... Sarah Michelle Gellar
XANDER HARRIS......................... Nicholas Brendon
RUPERT GILES.......................... Anthony S. Head
WILLOW ROSENBERG...................... Alyson Hannigan
CORDELIA CHASE........................ Charisma Carpenter
ANGEL................................. David Boreanaz

SPIKE.............................*James Marsters
DRUSILLA..........................*Juliet Landau
OZ................................*Seth Green
KENDRA............................*Bianca Lawson
POLICE LADY.......................*Spice Williams
MR. PFISTER.(WORM GUY).............*Kelly Connell
WILLY.............................*Saverio Guerra
HOSTAGE KID.......................*Danny Strong

BUFFY THE VAMPIRE SLAYER

"What's My Line? - Part Two"

SET LIST

INTERIORS

SUNNYDALE HIGH SCHOOL
    HALL
    LIBRARY
        GILES' OFFICE
    LOUNGE
    CLASSROOM

BUFFY'S HOUSE
    FOYER
    *KITCHEN/DINING ROOM
    CELLAR
FACTORY
    DRUSILLA'S BEDROOM
ANGEL'S APARTMENT
WILLY'S ALIBI ROOM
    STORAGE ROOM
    ADJACENT ROOM
SEWER
CHURCH
    FOYER

EXTERIORS

*SUNNYDALE HIGH SCHOOL
    *COLONNADE
    *COURTYARD
BUFFY'S HOUSE
CHURCH (STOCK)

BUFFY THE VAMPIRE SLAYER

"What's My Line? -Part Two"   *

TEASER

FADE IN:

1 INT. ANGEL'S APARTMENT - EARLY MORNING   1

Remember BUFFY and that chick who says she's the NEW SLAYER?
They're still staring at each other, breathing hard. The
Apartment is in major shambles.

                    BUFFY
          Let's start again. You're the who?

The new slayer radiates poise and intensity. She's a "take-
no-guff" gal with a faintly regal air about her.

                    KENDRA
          I'm the slayer.

                    BUFFY
          Nice cover story. Here's a tip - try
          it on someone who's not the real
          slayer.

                    KENDRA
          You can't stop me. Even if you kill
          me, another slayer will be sent to
          take my place.

                    BUFFY
          Could you stop with the slayer thing?
          I'm the damn slayer!

                    KENDRA
          Nonsense. There is but one - and I
          am she.

Buffy takes this in, truly puzzled. Kendra is so annoyingly
earnest. Finally-

                    BUFFY
          Okay... Scenario: I back off. You
          promise not to go all wiggy until we
          go to my watcher and figure out what
          this is all about.

                    KENDRA
          Wiggy?

                                                    CONTINUED

1 CONTINUED: 1

                         BUFFY
          You know - no kicko, no fighto?

A beat as Kendra considers. Then-

                         KENDRA
          I accept your scenario.

They let their arms down, circling each other, exhausted from
the fight and harboring a good amount of suspicion and
contempt.

                         KENDRA (cont'd)
          Your English is very odd, you know.

                         BUFFY
          Yeah - it's something about being
          woken by an axe. Makes me talk all
          crazy.
                    (then)
          So you were sent here?

                         KENDRA
          Yes, by my Watcher.

                         BUFFY
          To do what, exactly?

                         KENDRA
          To do my duty. I am here to kill
          vampires.

2 INT. SEEDY BAR STORAGE ROOM - EARLY MORNING   2

CLOSE ON

A window HIGH on the wall of the storage room. The SUN
streams through the barred glass, spilling light into the
room.

We hear the labored breathing of someone in pain as we

WIDEN

to reveal ANGEL huddled in a corner of the storage room. The
sun angles across the floor - leaving him only a small patch
of safety. And every passing minute brings the sun closer to
him.

CONTINUED

2 CONTINUED: 2

CLOSE ON ANGEL

Sweating. The walls are definitely closing in. He's trying
hard to maintain.

                              BLACKOUT.

               END OF TEASER

ACT ONE

3 INT. LIBRARY - MORNING   3

GILES paces in front of Buffy and Kendra - trying to make
heads or tails of the situation. When speaking to Giles,
Kendra is extremely respectful. Almost subservient.

                    GILES
               (to Kendra)
          Your watcher is Sam Zabuto, you say?

                    KENDRA
          Yes, sir.

                    GILES
          We've never met - but he is very well
          respected.

                    BUFFY
          What? So he's a real guy? As in,
          non-fictional?

                    GILES
          And what are you called?

                    KENDRA
          I am the vampire slayer.

                    BUFFY
               (irked)
          We got that part. He means your
          name.

                    NEW SLAYER
          Oh. They call me Kendra, only. I
          have no last name, sir.

                    BUFFY
          Can you say - stuck in the 80's?

                    GILES
          Buffy - please. There has obviously
          been some kind of misunderstanding
          here.

WILLOW enters the library at this point, startling everyone.

                    WILLOW
          Hey-

Kendra immediately advances on Willow - about to attack.

CONTINUED

3 CONTINUED: 3

                         KENDRA
                Identify yourself!

Buffy quickly stops Kendra - gives her a withering look.

                         BUFFY
                Back off, Pink Ranger. This is my
                friend-

                         KENDRA
                Friend?

                         BUFFY
                You know. Person you hang with?
                Amigo?

                         KENDRA
                I - I don't understand.

Buffy rolls her eyes - turns to Giles.

                         BUFFY
                You try. I'm tapped.

                         GILES
                Kendra. There are a few people,
                civilians if you will, who know
                Buffy's identity. Willow is one of
                them. And they also spend time
                together. Socially.

Kendra takes this in. Understanding, but still puzzled.

                         KENDRA
                And you allow this, sir?

                         GILES
                Well, you see...

                         KENDRA
                But, the slayer must work in secret.
                For security-

                         GILES
                Of course. With Buffy, however,
                it's... Some flexibility is required-

                         KENDRA
                Why?

                         WILLOW
                    (enough already)
                Hi guys. What's going on?

                                                      CONTINUED

3 CONTINUED: (2)

> BUFFY
> There's been a big mix-up.

> GILES
> It seems, that somehow, another
> slayer has been sent to Sunnydale.

> WILLOW
> Is that even possible? I mean, two
> slayers at the same time?

> GILES
> Not that I know of. The new slayer
> is only called after the previous
> slayer has died-
> (then/realizing)
> Good lord... You _were_ dead, Buffy.

> BUFFY
> (defensive)
> I was only gone for a minute.

> GILES
> Clearly, it doesn't matter how long
> you were gone. You were physically
> dead, causing the activation of the
> next slayer.

> KENDRA
> She... died?

> BUFFY
> Just a _little_.

> GILES
> Yes, she drowned. But she was
> revived.

> WILLOW
> So there really are two of them?

> GILES
> It would appear so. Yes.

Giles sits. Stunned.

> GILES (cont'd)
> We have no precedent for this. I'm
> quite flummoxed.

CONTINUED

                              BUFFY
          What's the flum? It's a mistake.
          She isn't supposed to be here. She
          goes home.
                    (to Kendra)
          No offense. But, I'm not dead and
          it's a teeny bit creepy having you
          around.

                              KENDRA
          I cannot simply leave. I was sent
          here for a reason. Mr. Zabuto said
          all the signs indicate that a very
          dark power is about to rise in
          Sunnydale.

                              GILES
          He's quite right. I'll need to
          contact him.

                              BUFFY
          So what was your plan for fighting
          this dark power? Just sort of attack
          people till you found a bad one?

                              KENDRA
          Of course not.

                              BUFFY
          Then why the hell did you jump me?

                              KENDRA
                    (sheepish)
          I thought you were a vampire.

The others look at each other.

                              BUFFY
          Oooh, a swing and a miss for the
          rookie.

                              KENDRA
          I had good reason to think you were.
          Did I not see you kissing a vampire?

                              WILLOW
          Buffy would never do that! Oh -
                    (turns to Buffy)
          - except for - that sometimes you do
          that.
                              (more)

                                                        CONTINUED

3 CONTINUED: (4)

                    WILLOW (cont'd)
               (to Kendra)
          But only with Angel!
               (to Buffy)
          Right?

                    BUFFY
          <u>Yes</u> right.
               (to Kendra)
          You saw me with Angel. He's a
          vampire but he's good.

                    KENDRA
          Angel? You mean Angelus? I've read
          of him. He is a <u>monster</u>.

                    GILES
          No, no, he's good now.

                    WILLOW
          Really.

                    BUFFY
          He had a gypsy curse.

                    KENDRA
          Oh.
               (beat)
          He had a what?

                    BUFFY
          Just trust me. Angel's on the home
          team now. Wouldn't hurt a fly.

                    KENDRA
          I cannot believe you. He looked to
          me like just another animal when I -

She stops. Buffy eyes her, worried.

                    BUFFY
          When you what? What did you do to
          him?

                    KENDRA
          I...

                    BUFFY
          What did you <u>do</u>?

4 INT. SEEDY BAR STORAGE ROOM - DAY   4

Now Angel's patch of shadow is nothing but a sliver. Sun
fills the room.

Angel has his jacket pulled over his head - taking what
little protection it can provide. He is literally
smouldering now - only moments away from total combustion.

Then the door to the storage room SLAMS open.

CLOSE ON ANGEL'S LEGS

As a pair of MALE hands grabs them and TUGS.

WIDEN to reveal-

WILLY, the snitch, dragging Angel across the floor of the
stockroom. He pulls him out of the light and into-

5 INT.   ADJACENT ROOM - CONTINUOUS - DAY   5

Willy leans down, lifts a TRAP DOOR opening in the floor,
pushes Angel's near lifeless body into-

6 INT. SEWER - CONTINUOUS - DAY   6

Where Angel drops into the water, Willy following, lowers
himself to find-

None other than SPIKE, who waits with a few of his minions.

                    WILLY
          Here you go, friend. A little singed
          around the edges, maybe, but he'll be
          good as new in a day or so.

We see that Angel is terribly weak and nearly unconscious.
Spike reaches for Angel - but Willy tugs his hand away.

                    WILLY (cont'd)
          Hey now. We had a deal.

Spike gives Willy a look. Pulls a wad from his pocket and
starts to peel off some bills - hands them to Willy.

                    SPIKE
          What's the matter, Willy. Don't
          trust me?

Willy is counting the bills. Indicates that Spike owes him
a few more.

                                                    CONTINUED

6 CONTINUED: 6

                         WILLY
          Like a brother.

Spike holds the last bill up - makes Willy reach for it.

                         SPIKE
          Talk and I'll have your guts for
          garters.

                         WILLY
          Wild horses couldn't drag it.

Spike drops the bill in the water.

                         SPIKE
          Oops. Sorry - friend.

Willy fishes for the bill. The minions start to gather up
Angel.

                         WILLY
          What're you gonna do with him, anyway?

                         SPIKE
          I'm thinking - maybe dinner and a
          movie. I don't want to rush into
          anything. I've been hurt, you know.

Spike strides away, exiting round a bend in the tunnel. His
minions follow with Angel, leaving Willy behind.

7 INT. BUFFY'S HOUSE - FOYER - DAY   7

CORDELIA stands with WORM GUY, examining a lipstick. Worm
Guy has an open satchel full of cosmetics and creams at his
side.

                         CORDELIA
          Do you have this in raisin? I know
          you wouldn't think so - but I'm both
          a winter and a summer-

Worm Guy just looks at her. Creepy and unblinking. Finally-

                         WORM GUY
          $9.99, tax included.

                         CORDELIA
          You - You said that already. Do you
          have anything in the berry family?

                                                      CONTINUED

7 CONTINUED: 7

Worm Guy doesn't respond. He simply takes the lipstick from
Cordelia. Drops it back in the bag.

                         WORM GUY
               Are there more ladies in the house?

                         CORDELIA
               They aren't home.
                         (then)
               Nothing personal - but maybe you
               should look into selling dictionaries-

She stops as she sees a SINGLE WORM appears from under WORM
GUY'S COAT and skitter across the floor. Cordelia backs away
with a gasp. She looks at WORM GUY - who stares back at her,
impassive. He looks totally human. Odd, but human.

XANDER comes down the stairs - seeing worm dude for the first
time.

                         XANDER
               Hey. What's up?

Cordelia grabs Xander by the arm - freaked.

                         CORDELIA
               He's a... salesman. But he was just
               leaving.
                         (to Worm Guy)
               Right?

WORM GUY just stands there.

                         CORDELIA (cont'd)
               Okay. Bye bye. Thanks.

Nothing. Xander moves to hustles him out.

                         XANDER
               Come on, Mary Kay. Time to-

As Xander approaches, WORM GUY'S FACE starts to RIPPLE.
Undulate, in fact. As though there were creepy crawly things
UNDER his skin.

                         XANDER (cont'd)
               Time to...

He turns to Cordelia - calmly.

                         XANDER (cont'd)
               Run.

                                                          CONTINUED

7   CONTINUED: (2)   7

     Worm Guy stands between them and the front door, so they BOLT
     in the opposite direction. WORM GUY suddenly SHIFTS - his
     human form falling away as he DECOMPOSES into THOUSANDS of
     horrible crawly worms - who stream after Cordy and Xander.

8   INT. BUFFY'S HOUSE - KITCHEN/DINING ROOM - CONT. - DAY   8

     Xander and Cordelia run past the stairs for the back door,
     but Pfister has reformed and is BLOCKING THEIR PATH. They
     have no alternative but to duck into the CELLAR.

9   INT. BUFFY HOUSE - CELLAR - CONTINUOUS - DAY   9

     Xander and Cordelia jam into the cellar. They shut and bolt
     the door. The worms simply flow through the crack under the
     door. Cordelia SCREAMS.

     Xander grabs an old broom and starts to beat them off.

                         XANDER
                 Find something to block the crack
                 under the door!

     Cordelia frantically searches - yelping as she brushes worms
     off her. Finally, she comes across some DUCT TAPE. She
     pushes it into Xander's hands.

                         CORDELIA
                 I - I don't- do worms-

     He shoves the broom at her.

                         XANDER
                 Cover me.

     Cordelia kills worms while Xander, grimacing, TAPES THE
     CRACKS AROUND THE DOOR. Then he and Cordy kill the remaining
     critters. The worms are momentarily thwarted.

     A beat. Xander and Cordelia look around the cellar. There
     are NO WINDOWS. And the only door is the one they came in.

                         XANDER (cont'd)
                 You know - just when you think you've
                 seen it all. Along comes a worm guy.

10   INT. SEEDY BAR STORAGE ROOM/BAR - DAY   20

     Freaked-out and breathing hard, Buffy BURSTS into the storage
     room - only to find it empty.

                                                            CONTINUED

> BUFFY
> Angel -?

Kendra enters, moves around the room.   Checking the floor.

> KENDRA
> No ashes.

> BUFFY
> What?

> KENDRA
> When a vampire combusts, he leaves
> ashes.

> BUFFY
> Yeah, I know the drill.

> KENDRA
> So I did not kill him.

> BUFFY
> And I don't have to kill you.

A glare moment for the girls. Willy enters, momentarily
unseen.

> WILLY
> Whoah, there's a lot of tension in
> this room.

Before he can speak another word KENDRA CHARGES HIM.
Slamming him into a table and drawing her fist back for a
mighty blow-

CLOSE ON KENDRA & BUFFY

As BUFFY catches her hand mid-flight. She looks at Kendra,
exasperated.

> BUFFY
> Doesn't anyone just say "hello" where
> you come from?

Kendra keeps her grip on Willy firm.

> KENDRA
> This one is dirty. I can feel it.

CONTINUED

                         BUFFY
          That's nice for you, percepto girl.
          But we're not going to get anything
          out of him if he's oh, say,
          unconscious.

Buffy grabs Willy away from Kendra. Addresses him - hard.

                         BUFFY (cont'd)
          Where is Angel?

                         WILLY
          My bud, Angel? You think I'd let him
          fry? I saved him in the nick. He
          was about five minutes away from
          being a crispy critter.

Buffy shoots Kendra a vicious look.

                         BUFFY
          Where did he go? Home?

                         WILLY
          Uh, he said he was gonna stay
          underground. You know, recuperate.

                         BUFFY
          Are you telling me the truth?

                         WILLY
          I swear! I swear on my mother's
          grave should something fatal happen
          to her god forbid.

                         KENDRA
          Then he is all right. We can return
          to your Watcher for our orders.

                         BUFFY
          Orders? I don't take orders. I do
          things my way.

                         KENDRA
          No wonder you died.

                         BUFFY
          Let's go.

As they start out.

                                                    CONTINUED

10 CONTINUED: (3)   10

                    WILLY
      I have to ask if either of you girls
      has considered modeling. I got a
      friend with a camera, strictly high
      class nude work - art photographs,
      but naked.

The look they give him is the first thing they have ever
shared.

                    WILLOW
      You don't have to answer right away...

They exit.

11 INT. DRUSILLA'S BEDROOM - DAY   11

DRU is in bed, looking gravely (so to speak) ill. Spike
enters, sits on her bed. Strokes her brow until she wakes.

                  DRUSILLA
      Ah. I was dreaming-

                  SPIKE
      Of what, pet?

                  DRUSILLA
      Beautiful. We were in Paris. You
      had a branding iron...

                  SPIKE
      I brought you something-

Drusilla nods, out of it, as Spike steps out of the room.

                  DRUSILLA
      And there were worms in my baguette...

Spike reenters with ANGEL - who is bound and gagged.

                  SPIKE
      Your sire, my sweet.

Drusilla's expression immediately brightens.

                  DRUSILLA
      Angel?

Spike roughly throws Angel into the corner.

CONTINUED

                         SPIKE
          The one and only. Now all we need is
          the new moon tonight. Then he will
          die and you will be fully restored-

Spike moves back to Dru on the bed - excited.

                         SPIKE (cont'd)
          My black goddess. My ripe, wicked
          plum. It's been-

                         DRUSILLA
          Forever.

Drusilla smiles, pulls him close. They kiss hungrily.

CLOSE ON ANGEL

He looks away. Disgusted and ashamed of what he did to Dru.

ON SPIKE AND DRUSILLA

They finally come up for air-

                         DRUSILLA (cont'd)
          Let me have him. Until the moon.

Spike, glances at Angel, doesn't like the idea - but can't
deny Drusilla her request.

                         SPIKE
          Alright then, you can play. But
          don't kill him. He musn't die until
          the ritual.

Drusilla sits up.

                         DRUSILLA
          Bring him to me.

Spike yanks Angel off the floor. Dru gets up on her knees,
moves to him, unties the gag. Tenderly runs her fingers over
his face. Angel won't make eye contact. But Dru grabs his
head - turns it until he's forced to look at her. She frowns.

                         DRUSILLA (cont'd)
          You've been a very bad daddy.

                                              CONTINUED

11 CONTINUED: (2)   11

And she SLAPS him with wicked force.

BLACKOUT.

END OF ACT ONE

ACT TWO

12 EXT. SCHOOL - COLONNADE - DAY   12   *

       Buffy, Kendra, Giles and Willow are gathered.

                         GILES
               Kendra, I've conferred with your
               Watcher, Mr. Zabuto. He and I agree
               that until this matter with Spike and
               Drusilla is resolved, you two should
               work together.

                         BUFFY
               Oh, that'll be a treat.

                         KENDRA
               So you believe that Spike is
               attempting to revive this Drusilla to
               health?

                         GILES
               Yes. That would be the dark power
               your Watcher referred to. Drusilla
               is not just evil. She's also quite
               mad. Restored to her full heath
               there is absolutely no telling what
               she might do.

                         KENDRA
               Then we will stop Spike.

                         BUFFY
               Good plan! Let's go! Charge!

                         GILES
               Buffy-

                         BUFFY
                    (to Kendra)
               It's a little more complicated than
               that, okay, John Wayne?

                         GILES
               Yes, I'm afraid it is. Spike has
               called out the Order of Taraka to
               keep Buffy out of the way.

                         KENDRA
               The assassins? I read of them in the
               writings of Dramius.

                                                      CONTINUED

                    GILES
          Really? Which volume?

                    KENDRA
          I believe it was six, sir.

                    BUFFY
               (to Kendra)
          How do you know that stuff?

                    KENDRA
          From my studies.

                    BUFFY
          So - you have a lot of free time.

                    KENDRA
          I study because it is required. The
          slayer handbook insists on it.

                    WILLOW
          There's a slayer handbook?

                    BUFFY
          Handbook? What handbook? How come
          I didn't get a handbook?

                    WILLOW
          Is there a T-shirt too?
               (off their looks)
          Cause, that would be cool...

                    GILES
          After meeting you, Buffy, I was quite
          sure the handbook would be of no use
          in your case.

                    BUFFY
          What do you mean - "it would be of no
          use in my case?" What's wrong with
          my case?

Giles turns his attention back to Kendra.

                    GILES
          Kendra - perhaps you could show me
          the bit in Dramius six about the
          Order of Taraka. I must admit, I
          could never get through that book.

                    KENDRA
          Yes, it was difficult. All those
          footnotes!

12 CONTINUED: (2)   12

They laugh. Buffy looks at Willow.

                    BUFFY
               (sotto)
          Hello and welcome to planet pocket
          protector.

Kendra and Giles move off, but Giles stops - turns to Buffy.

                    GILES
          Oh, Buffy. Principal Snyder came
          snooping around for you.

                    BUFFY
          Eeee, the career fair.

                    GILES
          You'd best make an appearance, I
          think.

                    BUFFY
          Right.

                    KENDRA
          Buffy's a student here?

                    GILES
          Yes.

A beat as Kendra takes this in. Then, coolly-

                    KENDRA
          Right. Of course. I'd imagine
          she's a cheerleader, too.

                    GILES
          Actually, she gave up cheerleading.
          It's a funny story, really...

Kendra just looks at him. Clearly, Buffy's wacky life does
not amuse.

                    GILES (cont'd)
          Let's go find that book, shall we?

They move off to the library. Willow and Buffy watch,
somewhat stunned.

                    BUFFY
          Get a load of the She-Giles.

                    WILLOW
          Creepy.

                                                    CONTINUED

12   CONTINUED: (3)   12

     They gather their stuff, move for the door.

13   EXT. SCHOOL - COURTYARD - DAY   13   *

                         BUFFY
          I bet Giles wishes I were more of a
          fact geek.

                         WILLOW
          Giles is enough of a fact geek for
          both of you.

                         BUFFY
          But you saw how he and Kendra were
          vibing. "Volume six - ha, ha, ha!"

                         WILLOW
          Buffy. No one can replace you.
          You'll always be Giles' favorite.

                         BUFFY
          I wonder...

                         WILLOW
          Of course you will. You're his
          slayer. The real slayer.

                         BUFFY
          No - I mean, I wonder if it would be
          so bad. Being replaced.

                         WILLOW
          You mean, like, letting Kendra take
          over?

                         BUFFY
          Maybe. It would be wild if, after
          this thing with Spike and the
          assassins is over, I could say -
          "Kendra, you slay. I'm going to
          Disneyland..."

                         WILLOW
          But not forever, right?

                         BUFFY
          No, Disneyland would get boring after
          a few months. But I could do...
          other stuff. Any stuff. Career day
          stuff. Who knows, Willow, I might
          even be able to have, like, a normal
          life...

                                                              CONTINUED

13 CONTINUED: 13

    Off Buffy's hopeful face.

14 INT. BUFFY HOUSE - CELLAR - DAY   14

    Xander and Cordy are still in their man/worm stand-off.
    Xander is sitting on the floor while Cordelia, totally
    wigging, paces.

                    XANDER
        Think you could sit down or change
        your pattern or something? You're
        making me queasy.

                  CORDELIA
        Because you're just sitting there.
        You should be thinking up a plan.

                    XANDER
        I do have a plan. We wait. Buffy
        saves us.

                  CORDELIA
        How will she even know where to find
        us?

                    XANDER
        Cordelia. This is Buffy's house.
        Odds are - she'll find us.

                  CORDELIA
        What if she doesn't? I'm supposed to
        just waste away down here with _you_?
        No thank you.

    She moves toward the stairs to the door - Xander leaps up.

                    XANDER
        What are you doing?

                  CORDELIA
        Checking to see if he's gone-

                    XANDER
        That's brilliant. What if he isn't?

                  CORDELIA
        Oh - Right. You think we should just
        slack here and hope that somebody
        else decides to be a hero. Sorry,
        forgot I was stranded with a _loser-_

                                                CONTINUED

14 CONTINUED: 14

                    XANDER
          And yet, I never forgot that I was
          stuck with the numb-brain who let Mr.
          Mutant into the house in the first
          place-

                    CORDELIA
          He looked normal -!

                    XANDER
          What - he was supposed to have an
          arrow and the word ASSASSIN over his
          head? All it took was the prospect
          of a free makeover and you licked his
          hand like a big, dumb DOG!

                    CORDELIA
          You know what? I'm going. I'd
          rather be worm food than look at your
          pathetic face-

                    XANDER
          Then go. I won't stop you-

They are toe to toe now. Seething-

                    CORDELIA
          I bet you you wouldn't. I bet you'd
          just let a girl go off to her doom
          all by herself-

                    XANDER
          Not just any girl. You're special-

                    CORDELIA
          I can't believe I'm stuck here
          spending what are probably my last
          moments on earth with you!

                    XANDER
          I hope these are my last moments!
          Three more seconds of you and I'm
          gonna-

                    CORDELIA
          You're gonna what? Coward!

                    XANDER
          Moron!

                    CORDELIA
          I hate you!

                                        CONTINUED

14 CONTINUED: (2)   14

                        XANDER
              I hate you!

A beat. They FALL INTO A KISS. A kiss of steel-melting,
ground-shaking intensity. It just goes on and on and on...

Finally, they break. LEAP apart as if they've been
electrocuted. A beat. Then-

                        XANDER (cont'd)
              We so need to get out of here.

Without hesitation, Cordelia RIPS AWAY the tape that seals
the door.

                        CORDELIA
              He's gone.

Xander THROWS the door open and they BOLT.   As soon as
they've crossed from the kitchen through the dining room -
HUNDREDS OF WORMS RAIN DOWN ON THEM FROM ABOVE.

15 EXT. BUFFY'S HOUSE - CONTINUOUS - DAY   15

Xander and Cordelia race out the front door. Xander, well
ahead, is relatively worm-free. Then he looks back and sees
Cordelia falling to the ground, COVERED in worms.

                        CORDELIA
              Help! Help me!

Xander races to a nearby garden hose and turns the pressure
up as far as it will go.

Cordelia is flailing as Xander TURNS THE HOSE ON HER. She
YELLS and fights the water, but it works - the worms are
washed away. Xander runs to her and lifts her to her feet.

They bolt for Cordy's car. They get in and SPEED OFF.

16 INT. SCHOOL LOUNGE - DAY   16

Willow and Buffy stand amid the hubbub of CAREER WEEK,
looking at a large schedule of events that's posted on the
wall.

                        BUFFY
              Okay, my tests say I should be
              looking into law enforcement - duh -
              and environmental design...

                                                        CONTINUED

16 CONTINUED: 16

                         WILLOW
          Environmental design? That's
          landscaping, right?

                         BUFFY
                    (shrugs)
          I checked the shrub box. Landscaping
          was yesterday - so law it is.

They start to move through the career seekers. Buffy notices
OZ, who is standing nearby, staring at Willow intently. He
carries his guitar case.

                         BUFFY (cont'd)
          Don't look now, Will, but that guy
          over there is totally checking you.

Willow glances over to OZ - waves it away.

                         WILLOW
          Oh. That's Oz. He's just expressing
          computer nerd solidarity.

                         BUFFY
          Really? Then why is he on his way
          over?

Oz approaches. Eyes only for Willow.

                         OZ
          Hi.

Buffy smiles, keeps moving.

                         BUFFY
                    (to Willow)
          Told you.

Willow stays behind with OZ - while Buffy heads toward the
LAW ENFORCEMENT BOOTH.

                         OZ
          Hey.

                         WILLOW
          Hey.

                         OZ
          Did you decide? Are you gonna become
          a corporate computer suit guy?

                                           CONTINUED

                        WILLOW
          Uh, I think I'm gonna finish high
          school first. What about you.

                        OZ
          I'm not really a computer person. Or
          a work of any kind person.

                        WILLOW
          Then why'd they select you?

                        OZ
          I sort of test well. Which is cool,
          except then it leads to jobs.

                        WILLOW
          Well, don't you have some ambition?

                        OZ
          Oh, yeah. E flat, diminished 9th.

                        WILLOW
          Huh?

                        OZ
          The E flat's doable, but it's that
          diminished 9th... that's a man's
          chord. You could lose a finger.

He smiles. Willow smiles too - not sure what to make of him.

ON BUFFY

Who is now over at the LAW ENFORCEMENT BOOTH. The STERN
POLICE LADY is there. She sees Buffy, nods to a sign-in
sheet. Buffy adds her name and Police Lady takes the paper.

                        POLICE LADY
          Listen up and answer when I call your
          name!-

Buffy and the other seminar attendees gather around.

                        POLICE LADY (cont'd)
          Buffy Summers!

                        BUFFY
          Here.

Without a beat - POLICE LADY DRAWS A SERIOUS-LOOKING GUN and
AIMS AT BUFFY. Buffy DIVES FOR COVER as she SHOOTS!

CONTINUED

                        BUFFY (cont'd)
      Get down!

MAYHEM. All the career day folks FREAK as Police Lady shoots
AGAIN AND AGAIN at BUFFY.

ON OZ AND WILLOW

Bullets FLY past them.

                        OZ
      Look out!

OZ THROWS HIMSELF OVER WILLOW - TAKING HER TO THE GROUND. A
BULLET GRAZES HIS ARM.

They land hard. Oz on top of her, bleeding.

BUFFY

CRAWLS ON THE GROUND THROUGH THE CHAOS, moving out of POLICE
LADY'S line of sight until she ends up BEHIND HER. Buffy
GRABS POLICE LADY'S LEGS FROM UNDER HER, dropping her.

POLICE LADY and BUFFY ROLL ON THE GROUND. Buffy finally
manages to get the GUN OUT OF HER HAND and it skitters away.

At which point - Police Lady simply DRAWS ANOTHER GUN.
Points it right at Buffy's face.

But before Police Lady can shoot - a FOOT KICKS THE GUN FROM
HER HAND. Buffy looks up to see KENDRA, ready to kick some
lady-in-blue butt. Buffy takes advantage of the distraction
and POUNDS POLICE LADY repeatedly in the face-

Still, Police Lady manages to throw Buffy off her and grab
ONE OF THE KIDS who was at the law enforcement booth before
Buffy or Kendra can stop her. She's GOT YET ANOTHER gun -
which she points at the poor kid's chest.

                        BUFFY
      Don't!

Hostage in tow, Police Lady backs out of the lounge. She
gets to the door, TOSSES the kid to the ground and exits.

Kendra goes after Police Lady while Buffy runs to OZ and
WILLOW.

                                        CONTINUED

16 CONTINUED: (4)   16

                         WILLOW
                    (to Buffy)
               He's, he's shot-
                    (to OZ)
               Are you okay?

                         OZ
               I'm shot. Wow. It's very... odd.
               And painful.

Kendra runs back into the room. Moves to Buffy.

                         KENDRA
               She's gone.

A stunned beat as people emerge from their hiding spots.
What just happened here? The hostage kid stands - shaky.

                         HOSTAGE KID
               Was - was that a demonstration?

17 INT. LIBRARY - DAY   17

     Buffy, Kendra, Giles and Willow are doing the post-seige
     analysis.

                         BUFFY
                    (to Giles)
               She was definitely one of the Taraka
               gang, Giles. And way gun happy.

                         GILES
                    (to Willow)
               And this Oz, he's alright?

                         WILLOW
               The paramedic said it was only a
               scrape, thank goodness-

She's interrupted by XANDER AND A VERY WET CORDELIA, who
enter. They're tripping from both worm dude and their
unscheduled lip-burst. Buffy glances at Kendra.

                         BUFFY
               Down girl-

But KENDRA is totally rooted - looking at Xander like a deer
caught in the headlights. Buffy's puzzled.

                         XANDER
               Who sponsored career day today - The
               British Soccer Fan Association?

                                                          CONTINUED

7 CONTINUED: 17

                         GILES
              We had a rather violent visit from
              one of the Order of Taraka-

                         XANDER
              You want to talk Order of Taraka? We
              met the <u>king freak</u> of the Order of-

Now he sees KENDRA - stops.

                         GILES
              Forgive me. Xander, Cordelia - this
              is Kendra. It's very complicated,
              but she is also a slayer-

Cordelia is too wigged-out to be newly fazed. She barely
glances at Kendra, sits.

                         CORDELIA
                      (to Kendra)
              Hi. Nice to meet you.

                         XANDER
                      (to Buffy)
              A slayer? I knew this "I'm the only
              one, I'm the only one" thing was just
              an attention getter.

                         BUFFY
              Just say hello, Xander.

Xander moves to Kendra, who appears mortified by his
attention. he notices her babe factor - vibes her.

                         XANDER
              Welcome. So you're a slayer, huh?
              I like that in a woman.

Kendra can only look at her shoes. Totally flustered.

                         KENDRA
              I - I, hope... I thank you. I mean,
              sir... I will be of service.

                         XANDER
              Good. Great. It's good to be a
              giver.

Xander looks to Buffy - what's with her? Buffy shrugs.

                         GILES
              This assassin you encountered,
              Xander. What did he look like?

                                                    CONTINUED

17 CONTINUED: (2)   17

Just then Cordelia SHRIEKS - finds a DEAD WORM in her hair.

                    XANDER
          Like that.

                    BUFFY
          You and bug people, Xander. What's
          up with that?

                    XANDER
          But this dude was different than the
          preying mantis lady. He was a man of
          bugs. Not a man who was a bug.

                    WILLOW
          Okay.
                    (then)
          Huh?

                    GILES
          The important thing is - everybody's
          okay. Still, it is quite apparent
          that we are under serious attack-

                    BUFFY
          Yeah. These Taraka guys are Uberbad.
          If Kendra hadn't been there today I
          would have been toast.

Kendra and Buffy exchange a look. The thanks noted.

                    GILES
          I fear the worse is yet to come.
          I've discovered the remaining keys to
          Drusilla's cure. The ritual requires
          her sire and must take place in a
          church on the night of the new moon-

                    KENDRA
          The new moon? But that is tonight.

                    GILES
          Exactly. I'm sure the assassins are
          here to kill Buffy before she can put
          a stop to things-

Buffy suddenly stands - her tone urgent.

                    BUFFY
          They need Drusilla's sire? You mean
          the vamp that made her?

                                                    CONTINUED

                    WILLOW
          What is it, Buffy?

                    BUFFY
               (painfully)
          It's Angel. He's Drusilla's sire.

                    XANDER
          Man! That guy got some major neck in
          his day-

          Willow HITS Xander. Xander shuts up. Kendra is clearly
          displeased - but holds her tongue.

                    BUFFY
               (to Giles)
          This thingy. This ritual. Will it
          kill him?

                    GILES
          I'm afraid so.

                    BUFFY
          We have to do something. We have to
          find the church where this ritual
          takes place-

                    GILES
          Agreed. And we must work quickly.
          There are only five hours to sundown.

                    WILLOW
          Don't worry, Buffy, we'll save Angel.

                    KENDRA
          Angel? Our priority must be to stop
          Drusilla.

                    XANDER
               (bridling)
          Angel's our friend. Except I don't
          like him.

                    BUFFY
          Look, you've got your priorities and
          I've got mine. Right now, they mesh.
          You gonna work with me or are you
          gonna get out of my way?

                    KENDRA
               (a beat)
          I am with you.

                                                    CONTINUED

17 CONTINUED: (4)   17

                         BUFFY
             Good. Cause I've had it. Spike is
             going down. You can attack me, you
             can send assassins after me... that's
             just fine. But nobody messes with my
             boyfriend.

                                        BLACKOUT.

                   END OF ACT TWO

ACT THREE

18 INT. DRUSILLA'S BEDROOM - NIGHT   18

CLOSE ON

Drusilla - looking much perkier - takes a small bottle of
HOLY WATER from an old lined box. She speaks dreamily -
savoring her memories.

                    DRUSILLA
          My mother ate lemons. Raw.

WIDEN TO REVEAL

The bedroom lit by candles. And ANGEL on the bed, tied to
the bedposts - his naked chest exposed.

Drusilla drifts over, kneels before him. She runs her hands
along his chest. There is obvious heat between them - heat
that Dru plays with just to watch him squirm.

                    DRUSILLA (cont'd)
          She said she loved the way they made
          her mouth tingle-

Dru lifts the bottle of holy water. Dribbles a bit on
Angel's chest. We can hear the HISS as the water burns his
skin. He grimaces but does not cry out.

                    DRUSILLA (cont'd)
          Little Anne - her favorite was
          custard... Brandied pears...

Another splash of holy water. A bit more this time. Angel
reacts - his pain the product of both remorse and the torture.

                    ANGEL
          Dru-

                    DRUSILLA
               (stern)
          Shhhhhh.
               (then)
          And pomegranates. They used to make
          her face and fingers all red-

And she pours nice and slow this time. He nearly cries out.

                    DRUSILLA (cont'd)
          Remember little fingers? Little
          hands?
               (more)

                                                    CONTINUED

                         DRUSILLA (cont'd)
                    (beat)
               Do you?

She obviously wants a reply now. Finally, through his pain-

                         ANGEL
               If I could- I-

                         DRUSILLA
                    (snapping)
               Bite your tongue... They used to
               eat. Cake. And eggs. And honey.
                    (sweet as can be)
               Until you came and ripped their
               throats out-

She gives him another, BIGGER dose of water. Angel writhes.
As he settles, Drusilla searches his face. The amazing
sorrow there. And, like quicksilver, she suddenly appears
vulnerable - genuinely lost.

                         DRUSILLA (cont'd)
               You remember?

                         ANGEL
               Yes.

                         DRUSILLA
               You remember that kind of hungry?

                         ANGEL
               Yes...

                         DRUSILLA
               You used to feed me.

Angels looks away - she's not talking food now.

                         DRUSILLA (cont'd)
               You think you don't have it in you
               now. But you do. I can feel it.

She THROWS A HUGE SPLASH OF HOLY WATER on his chest. Angel
finally SCREAMS in agony.

                         DRUSILLA (cont'd)
               I can almost taste it.

9 INT. LIBRARY - NIGHT   19

The whole gang is present. Willow is at the computer with
Giles watching as she scrolls through some information.

                    GILES
          There are forty three churches in
          Sunnydale? That seems a bit
          excessive.

                    WILLOW
          It's the extra evil vibe from the
          hellmouth. Makes people pray harder.

                    GILES
          Check and see if any of them are
          closed or abandoned.

Willow obliges. Giles carries a large book over to-

ON CORDELIA AND XANDER

Who are sitting side by side, looking through some sort of
demon "mug book" - both reeling from their lip-lock. Stiff
as boards, they avoid eye contact.

                    Xander
          We got demons. We got monsters. But
          no bug dude or Police Lady.

Giles hands them the book he holds.

                    GILES
          You should have better luck with
          this. There's a section devoted
          entirely to the Order of Taraka.

Xander leafs through the book.

20 INT. GILES' OFFICE - CONTINUOUD - NIGHT   20

Kendra looks out at the others, then over at Buffy, who is
checking and re-checking her weapons, clearly keyed up and
freaking about Angel.

                    KENDRA
          And those two, they also know you are
          the slayer.

                    BUFFY
          Yup.

                                        CONTINUED

                          KENDRA
                Did anyone explain to you what
                "secret identity" means?

                          BUFFY
                Nope. Must be in the handbook.
                Right after the chapter on
                personality removal.

There's no real rancor there - Buffy is too focussed. Kendra
picks up a crossbow, checks it out.

                          BUFFY (cont'd)
                Careful with that thing.

                          KENDRA
                Please. I am an expert in all
                weapons-

As she says it, the thing goes off in her hand, firing an
arrow into Giles' lamp. Kendra is startled, tries to cover.

                          GILES (O.S.)
                Is everything all right?

                          BUFFY
                Yeah, it's okay. Kendra killed the
                bad lamp.

                          KENDRA
                Sorry. This trigger mechanism is
                different.
                     (conciliatory)
                Perhaps when this is over you can
                show me how to work it.

                          BUFFY
                When this is over, I'm thinking
                pineapple pizza and teen video
                fest - possibly something from the
                Ringwald oeuvre.

                          KENDRA
                I'm not allowed to watch television.
                My Watcher says it promotes
                intellectual laziness.

                          BUFFY
                And he says it like it's a bad thing?

21 INT. LIBRARY - NIGHT   21

                         XANDER
               Here we go. I am the Bug Man, coo
               coo coo chu.

CLOSE ON

A drawing of WORM GUY. Round-faced, meek. Not too scary-
looking. But a magnified DETAIL of the drawing shows his
WORMY COMPOSITION. Yuck.

ON XANDER AND CORDELIA

                         XANDER (cont'd)
                    (finds something)
               Okay. Okay. He can only be killed
               when he's in his disassembled state.

He addresses Cordelia - as to a three-year-old.

                         XANDER (cont'd)
               Disassembled. That means when he's
               broken down into all his buggy parts-

Cordelia, annoyed, grabs the book from him.

                         CORDELIA
               I know what it means, dork head-

Xander tries to grab it back.

                         XANDER
               Dork head? You slash me with your
               words.

CLOSE ON THEIR HANDS

As they inadvertently TOUCH.

XANDER AND CORDELIA

                    XANDER & CORDELIA
               Arrrgggghhhh!

They jump away from each other as though they've been
electrocuted.

OFF WILLOW

Puzzled by their interaction.

22 INT. GILES' OFFICE - NIGHT   22

Kendra also hears the SCREAM, then looks at Buffy.

                    KENDRA
          Your life is very different than mine.

                    BUFFY
          You mean the part where I
          occasionally have one? Yeah, I guess
          it is.

                    KENDRA
          The things you do and have. I was
          taught distract from my calling.
          Friends. School. Even family.

                    BUFFY
          What do you mean - even family?

                    KENDRA
          My parents - they sent me to my
          watcher when I was very young.

                    BUFFY
          How young?

                    KENDRA
          I don't remember them, actually.
          I've seen pictures... But that's how
          seriously the calling is taken by my
          people. My mother and father gave me
          to my watcher because they believed
          that they were doing the right thing
          for me - and for the world. You see?

Buffy is shocked. But Kendra shuts down hard.

                    BUFFY
          Oh. I'm-

                    KENDRA
          Please. I don't feel sorry for
          myself. Why should you?

                    BUFFY
          It just sounds very lonely.

                    KENDRA
          Emotions are weakness, Buffy. You
          shouldn't entertain them.

                    BUFFY
          What? Kendra - my emotions give me
          power. They're total assets.

                                              CONTINUED

> KENDRA
> Maybe. For you. But I prefer to
> keep an even mind.

Kendra picks up a dagger, polishes it. Buffy considers this,
then-

> BUFFY
> Huh. I guess that explains it.

> KENDRA
> Explains what?

> BUFFY
> When we were fighting. You're
> amazing. Your technique. It's
> flawless. Better than mine-

> KENDRA
> I know.

> BUFFY
>   (bristles)
> Still - I would have kicked your butt
> in the end. And you know why? No
> imagination.

Kendra starts polishing the knife a little more intensely.

> KENDRA
> Really? You think so?

> BUFFY
> Yep. You're good. But power alone
> isn't enough. A great fighter goes
> with the flow. She knows how to
> improvise. Don't get me wrong, I
> mean, you have potential-

> KENDRA
> Potential...

Kendra puts the weapon down - furious. Gets in Buffy's face.

> KENDRA (cont'd)
> I could wipe the floor with you right
> now.

A beat. Buffy smiles.

> BUFFY
> That would be anger you're feeling.

CONTINUED

22 CONTINUED: (2)

                        KENDRA
                  (thrown off)
      What?

                        BUFFY
      You feel it, right? How the anger
      gives you fire? A slayer needs that.

Xander enters, grabs a book. Kendra instantly goes nonverbal
and shy again.

                        XANDER
      Scuze me, ladies
            (to Kendra)
      Nice knife.

He ducks out. Buffy looks at Kendra with some sympathy.

                        BUFFY
      I'm guessing dating isn't big with
      your Watcher either.

                        KENDRA
      I am not permitted to speak with boys.

                        BUFFY
      Unless you're pummelling them, right?
            (sudden thought)
      Wait a minute.

                        KENDRA
      What?

                        BUFFY
      That guy. The sleazoid you nearly
      decked in the bar.

                        KENDRA
      You think he might help us?

                        BUFFY
      I think we might make him.

23 INT. DRUSILLA'S BEDROOM - NIGHT   23

Drusilla is still on her knees before Angel, who is reeling
from the pain. She holds the dreaded HOLY WATER over him.

                        DRUSILLA
      Say uncle?

Angel looks away.

CONTINUED

3 CONTINUED: 23

                         DRUSILLA (cont'd)
                    Oh. That's right - you killed my
                    uncle.

Drusilla DOUSES HIM again as SPIKE enters the room, seeing
them in their compromising position. He isn't pleased.

                         SPIKE
                    That's it then. Off to the church.

Drusilla looks up at him - all innocence. She holds the
bottle of holy water out to him.

                         DRUSILLA
                    It makes pretty colors.

Spike is not interested. He moves to untie Angel, who is
keenly aware of Spike's jealousy.

                         SPIKE
                    I'll see him die soon enough. I've
                    never been much for the pre-show.

Angel speaks up.

                         ANGEL
                    Too bad. That's what Drusilla likes
                    best, as I recall.

                         SPIKE
                    What's that supposed to mean?

Angel looks to Drusilla - his tone surprisingly leering.

                         ANGEL
                    Ask her. She knows what I mean.

Drusilla smiles. Can't help herself.

                         SPIKE
                    Well?

                         DRUSILLA
                    Shhhhhhhhh. Bad dog.

                         ANGEL
                    You should let me talk, Dru. Sounds
                    like your boy could use some pointers.
                         (to Spike)
                    She likes to be teased-

Spike's had it. Hurts Angel in a way to be determined.

                                                     CONTINUED

                         SPIKE
               Keep your hole shut!

Angel's really hurting, but he keeps on nonetheless.

                         ANGEL
               Take care of her, Spike. The way she
               touched me just now... I can tell
               when she's not satisfied-

Spike RIPS Angel from his ties - lifts him to his feet.

                         SPIKE
               I said - shut up!

                         ANGEL
               Or maybe you two just don't have the
               fire that we did-

Spike's HAND FLIES TO ANGEL'S NECK. The other hand BREAKS AN
ARM OFF A STANDING CANDELABRA - INSTANT STAKE.

                         SPIKE
               That's ENOUGH.

Spike draws the stake back. Angel steels himself - a
heartbeat away from death.

                         DRUSILLA
               Spike - NO!

Spike STIPS himself, not a moment too soon. Looks at Angel.
A beat and - incongruously - he smiles.

                         SPIKE
               Right. Right... You almost got me.

Spike puts the stake down. Collects himself.

                         SPIKE (cont'd)
               Aren't you a "throw himself to the
               lions" sort of sap these days?

SPIKE laughs. ROARS like a lion in Angel's face.

                         SPIKE (cont'd)
               Well, the lions are on to you, baby.
               If I kill you now - you go quick and
               Dru hasn't got a chance. And if Dru
               dies, your little Rebecca of
               SunnyHell farm and all her mates are
               spared her coming out party-

                                              CONTINUED

23 CONTINUED: (3)   23

Drusilla stands, eyes glowing with anticipation.

                    DRUSILLA
          Spike. The moon is rising. It's
          time.

She moves to Spike, who puts a territorial arm around her.

                    SPIKE
          Too bad, Angelus. Looks like you go
          the hard way - along with the rest of
          this miserable town.

24 INT. SEEDY BAR - NIGHT   24

SLAM! Willy is thrown against the wall by BUFFY. Kendra
PACES nearby.

                    WILLY
          Honest! I don't know where Angel is!

                    BUFFY
          How about this ritual tonight? What
          have you heard?

                    WILLY
          Nothing. It's all hush hush-

                    KENDRA
                (impatient)
          Just hit him, Buffy.

                    BUFFY
          She - likes to hit.

                    WILLY
          You know, maybe I did hear something
          about this ritual. Yeah... It's
          coming back to me... But I'd - I'd
          have to take you there-

Buffy lets Willy down. Starts to drag him toward the door.

                    BUFFY
          Let's go.

But Kendra hesitates.

                    KENDRA
          First, we must return to the watcher.

                                        CONTINUED

24 CONTINUED: 24

                              BUFFY
                    Excuse me? While we run to Giles,
                    the whole thing could go down-

                              KENDRA
                    But, it is procedure-

                              BUFFY
                    It's brainless, you mean! If we
                    don't go now - Angel could be history.

                              KENDRA
                    Is that all you're worried about?
                    Your boyfriend?

                              BUFFY
                    It's not all. But it's enough.

                              KENDRA
                    It's as I feared. He clouds your
                    judgement. We can't stop this ritual
                    alone-

                              BUFFY
                    He'll die-

Kendra finally loses her patience. Says what she's been
thinking all along.

                              KENDRA
                    He's a vampire. He should die! Why
                    am I the only person who sees it?

This hits Buffy hard. Her face goes cold. She grabs Willy
by the scruff of the neck.

                              BUFFY
                    Let's go.

She shoves him toward the door, heads out. Kendra calls out
after her.

                              KENDRA
                    Are you that big a fool?

Buffy looks back at Kendra with nothing but murder in her
eyes. Turns and heads out.

                              KENDRA (cont'd)
                         (softly, to herself)
                    Good riddance, then.

25 EXT. OLD ABANDONED CHURCH (STOCK) - NIGHT   25

    Establishing.

26 INT. CHURCH FOYER - NIGHT   26

        Willy leads Buffy into the dark vestibule.

                        WILLY
                Here you go. Don't ever say your
                friend Willy don't come through in a
                pinch-

        Buffy moves to follow, when out of the darkness appear WORM
        GUY, POLICE LADY and Spike's TWO VAMP HENCHMEN. They
        surround her. Willy turns to the VAMP HENCHMEN.

                        WILLY (cont'd)
                Here you go. Don't ever say your
                friend Willy don't come through in a
                pinch-

        Buffy reacts - oops. Make that MEGA OOPS.

                                        BLACKOUT.

                        END OF ACT THREE

ACT FOUR

The abandoned church hall is lit only by torches as the
ritual to heal Drusilla nears its peak. Spike swings the
senser as he reads grandly from the decoded book.

> SPIKE
> Eligor, I name thee. Bringer of war,
> poisoners, pariahs, grand obscenity!

Before him we now see ANGEL AND DRUSILLA, who stand face to
face, tied together by tight leather straps. Drusilla looks
up at Angel, her expression wild and expectant.

> SPIKE (cont'd)
> Eligor, wretched master of decay,
> bring your black medicine. Come
> restore your most impious, murderous
> child-

With gloved hands, Spike lifts THE RELIC - and pulls on the
base of the cross, UNSHEATHING A HIDDEN DAGGER. Smiles as
he grabs Angel's hand, which is BOUND TO DRUSILLA'S.

> SPIKE (cont'd)
> From the blood of the sire she is
> risen! From the blood of the sire
> shall she rise again!

Spike PLUNGES the knife through BOTH ANGEL and DRUSILLA'S
HANDS. Blood and a crackling, electric FORCE flows freely
between them.

Angel cries out, clearly in horrible pain. Drusilla,
however, delights in her wound - writhing in exquisite agony.
Spike claps his hands-

> SPIKE (cont'd)
> Right then! Now we let them come to
> a simmering boil, then remove to a
> low flame-

He's interrupted as the DOORS CRASH OPEN, revealing WILLY,
WORM GUY and BUFFY - who struggles against the iron grip of
LADY COP and the vampire henchmen. Spike is appalled but
Willy doesn't notice-

> WILLY
> It's pay day, pal. I got your slayer.

Spike advances on him, seething.

CONTINUED

                  SPIKE
        Are you tripping? You bring her
        here - now?

Buffy sees ANGEL and DRUSILLA, reacts. Angel is gone - can't
acknowledge her.

                  WILLY
        You said you wanted her-

                  SPIKE
        In the ground, pinhead! I wanted her
        <u>dead</u>-

                  WILLY
            (getting nervous)
        Now - now that's not what I heard.
        Word was, there was a bounty on her,
        dead or alive-

                  SPIKE
        You heard wrong, Willy.

                  BUFFY
            (to herself)
        Angel...

Spike is distracted by her. looks over where she looks.

                  SPIKE
        Yeah, it bugs me too, seeing 'em like
        that. Another five minutes and
        Angel'll be dead though, so I
        forebear. But don't feel too bad for
        Angel. He's got something you don't
        have.

                  BUFFY
        What.

                  SPIKE
        Five minutes. Patrice?

Police Lady raises a gun to Buffy's head.

The doors BURST OPEN, one of them actually coming off its
hinges. Kendra is handspringing across the room before
anyone even has time to react, smashing into Police Lady and
knocking her to the floor, her guy skittering away.

               SPIKE (cont'd)
        Who the hell is that?

                                                  CONTINUED

Buffy takes the moment to shake off her vamps.

                    BUFFY
          It's your lucky day, Spike.

Kendra grabs Spike-

                    KENDRA
          Two slayers.

Punches him, spinning him toward-

                    BUFFY
          No waiting.

Punches him, spinning him again. Kendra moves to punch him
again, but he ducks, engages her in fisticuffs as Police Lady
comes for Buffy, stilettos popping out from her sleeves.

ANGEL: THE VAMPS

Get up to get Buffy and Kendra - but one is arrowed from the
back. Giles is behind him, crossbow in hand. Willow and
Xander flank him, all armed. Xander looks, calls out to:

                    XANDER
          Hey larva boy!

WORM GUY turns, stares at Xander.

                    XANDER (cont'd)
          That's right. I'm talking to you -
          the big cootie.

WORM GUY has heard enough, starts for Xander/ Xander RACES
into the FOYER - shuts the door. Again WORM GUY sheds his human
form and devolves into worm state, streaming under the door-

28 INT. CHURCH FOYER - CONTINUOUS - NIGHT   28

CORDELIA is on the other side of the door and has spread some
kind of GLUE on the floor. She and XANDER watch as the WORMS
come under the door and GET STUCK.

                    XANDER
          Welcome, my pretties. Mwa haa haa!

He and Cordelia start to stomp on the worms. Xander goes at
it gleefully. Cordelia, a little gingerly.

                                              CONTINUED

28 CONTINUED:

ANGLE: SPIKE AND KENDRA

She's got the moves, but he's powerful - a couple of
crippling blows and he's got her on the defensive.

ANGLE: BUFFY AND POLICE LADY

Buffy is narrowly avoiding those knives. Looks over at
Kendra.

>   BUFFY
>   Switch!

Buffy backs into Kendra, grabs her by the arms and the two do
a tandem flip, sending Kendra flying into Police Lady.

>   SPIKE
>   Rather be fighting you anyway.

>   BUFFY
>   Mutual.

They fight.

ANGLE: GILES

As the vampire knocks the crossbow out of his hands and they
start wrestling, Willow jumping on his back.

ANGLE: XANDER AND CORDELIA

A stompin'. Cordy's totally into it now.

>   CORDELIA
>   Die! Die! Die!

>   XANDER
>   I think he did, Cordy...

ANGLE: SPIKE

Flies into a wall just as Willy is trying to exit thataway.
Grabs him.

>   SPIKE
>   Where are you going?

>   WILLY
>   There's a way in which this isn't my
>   fault.

>   SPIKE
>   They tricked you.

CONTINUED

>   WILLY
>   (outraged)
>   They were duplicitous!

>   SPIKE
>   Well, I'll only kill you just this
>   once.

He's about to - then sees:

ANGLE: BUFFY AT THE ALTAR

She grabs the handle of the knife, trying to pull it from
Angel and Drusilla's hands.

Spike tackles her from behind. Down they go.

ANGLE: WILLY

runs past Giles and Willow, who are finishing off the vamp
(Giles holds, Willow stakes). Willy then passes Xander and
Cordelia, who run in to join Giles and Willow.

ANGLE: KENDRA AND POLICE LADY

under the organ loft.

Police Lady knocks Kendra into a beam holding up the organ
loft. It gives slightly, just dust raining down. Not
sturdy. Police Lady slices Kendra in the arm, drawing blood.
Kendra looks at her shirt, getting angry.

>   KENDRA
>   That's my favorite shirt.
>   (thinks)
>   That's my only shirt!

Now she's pissed. She comes at Police Lady in a hail of
blows, finally knocking her out right under the organ loft at
the back.

ANGLE: SPIKE

Punches Buffy, gaining a moment to look about. Clearly, he's
out numbered. He pulls out the knife, cuts the bonds and
grabs Dru as Angel falls to the floor.

>   SPIKE
>   Sorry, dear, we gotta go. Hope that
>   was enough...

He grabs a torch by the altar and hurls it at Buffy's pals.
It hits an old curtain on the floor and starts a blaze.

                                                      CONTINUED

28   CONTINUED: (3)   28

He carries Dru on the other side of the fire to the back,
towards the organ loft.

ANGLE: BUFFY

Rises, pissed off. She grabs a CENSER and swings it over her
head. Throws it-

And it slams into the back of Spike's head. He stumbles
forward-

Right into the beam holding the organ loft up.

The beam falls, the loft crashes down on Spike and Dru.

ANGLE: BUFFY

                    BUFFY
          I'm good...

ANGLE: KENDRA

amongst Buffy's friends.

                    KENDRA
          She's good...

Buffy comes to Angel, the others joining her to help carry
him out. Kendra next to Buffy.

                    BUFFY
          It's gonna be okay...

                    ANGEL
          Buffy?

                    KENDRA
          Let's get him out.

They do, leaving the growing fire headed toward the rubble.

29   INT. SCHOOL LOUNGE - DAY   29

Willow enters, moves to OZ - who is at the snack machine, arm
in a sling. He sees her, brightens immediately.

                    OZ
          Oh. Hey. Animal cracker?

                    WILLOW
          No, thanks. How's your arm?

                                                    CONTINUED

                        OZ
          Suddenly painless.

                        WILLOW
          You can still play guitar okay?

                        OZ
          Not well, but not worse.

They start walking down the hall.

                        WILLOW
          You know, I never really thanked you-

                        OZ
          Please, don't. I don't do thanks.
          I get all red and I have to bail.
          It's not pretty.

                        WILLOW
          Then forget about - that thing.
          Especially the part where I kind
          of - owe you my life-

Oz can't take it. Pulls a cookie from the box.

                        OZ
          Look. Monkey. And he has a little
          hat. And pants.

Willow smiles - amused by his verbal juggling.

                        WILLOW
          Yeah. I see.

                        OZ
          The monkey is the only cookie animal
          that gets to wear clothes, you know
          that?-
                  (then/casual)
          You have the sweetest smile I've ever
          seen.

Willow is startled, but Oz breezes past it.

                        OZ (cont'd)
          So I'm wondering, do the other cookie
          animals feel sort of ripped? Like,
          is the hippo going - man, where are
          my pants?... I have my hippo
          dignity...

They turn a corner.

30   INT. SCHOOL HALLWAY - DAY   30

     Xander is moving through the hall when he sees Cordelia,
     coming his way. She sees him too. They both turn - head in
     the opposite direction. Then Xander thinks better of it.
     Turns back and runs to catch up with Cordelia.

                    XANDER
               We need to talk.

     He hustles her into an empty classroom.

31   INT. EMPTY CLASSROOM - DAY   31

     Xander and Cordelia stand a good distance from each other,
     arms folded.

                    XANDER
               Okay. Here's the deal. There is no
               reason for us to run every time we
               see each other in the halls.

                    CORDELIA
               Right. Okay.
                    (then)
               Why shouldn't we run?

                    XANDER
               What happened. There is a total
               explanation for it-

                    CORDELIA
               You're a pervert?

                    XANDER
               Me? I seem to recall that I was the
               jump_ee_, my friend-

                    CORDELIA
               As if! You've probably been planning
               this for months-

                    XANDER
                    (incredulous)
               Right. I hired a Latvian Bug Man to
               kill Buffy so I could kiss you. I
               hate to burst your bubble, but you
               don't inspire me to spring for dinner
               at Bucky's Fondue Hut.

                    CORDELIA
               Fine. Whatever. The point is,
               don't ever try it again-

                                                      CONTINUED

                    XANDER
          I didn't try it! Forget the bugs.
          Just the memory of your lips on mine
          makes my blood run cold-

                    CORDELIA
          If you dare breathe a word of this-

                    XANDER
          Like I want anyone to know!

                    CORDELIA
          Then it's erased?

                    XANDER
          Never happened.

                    CORDELIA
          Good.

                    XANDER
          Good!

And they FALL into each others arms. A smootchie!

32 INT. HALL OUTSIDE THE CLASSROOM - CONTINUOUS - DAY   32

A beat. Then we hear-

                    XANDER & CORDELIA (O.C.)
          Arrrrrrgggggghhhhh!

33 EXT. SCHOOL - DAY   33

Buffy and Kendra are walking outside the front of the school
toward the street. Kendra wears one of Buffy's shirts.

                    KENDRA
          Thank you for the shirt. It is very
          generous of you.

                    BUFFY
          Oh, hey, it looks better on -- well,
          me, but don't worry.

There is ease between them now -- Kendra smiles at the barb.

                    BUFFY (cont'd)
          Now, when you get to the airport --

                                                        CONTINUED

                    KENDRA
          I get on the plane with my ticket.
          And sit in a seat. Not the cargo
          hold.

                    BUFFY
          Very good.

                    KENDRA
          That is not traveling undercover.

                    BUFFY
          Exactly. Relax. You earned it. You
          sit. You eat the peanuts. You watch
          the movie, unless it's about a dog or
          Chevy Chase.

                    KENDRA
          I'll remember.

They arrive at the curb where a taxi waits.

                    BUFFY
          Thank you. For helping me save
          Angel.

                    KENDRA
          I am not telling my Watcher about
          that. it is too strange that a
          slayer loves a vampire.

                    BUFFY
          Tell me about it.

                    KENDRA
          Still, he is pretty cute.

                    BUFFY
          Well, then, maybe they won't fire me
          for dating him.

                    KENDRA
          You always do that.

                    BUFFY
          Do what?

                    KENDRA
          You talk about slaying like it's a
          job. It's not. It's who you are.

                    BUFFY
          You get that from the handbook?

                                                    CONTINUED

                    KENDRA
          From you.

                    BUFFY
          I guess I can't fight it. I'm a
          freak.

                    KENDRA
          But not the only freak.

                    BUFFY
          Not anymore.

A beat that turns awkward as Buffy moves forward --

                    KENDRA
          I don't hug.

                    BUFFY
          No. Good. Hate hugs.

Kendra gets in the taxi. Buffy watches it pull away.

34 INT. CHURCH - NIGHT   34

A mess. Black rubble everywhere.

CLOSE ON A PILE OF DEBRIS

From which a pale, sooty hand emerges.

ANOTHER HAND

Reaches down, grasps the buried hand by the wrist. Tugs.

WIDEN TO REVEAL

DRUSILLA - but unlike the Drusilla we've known. She is
RADIANT with good health. Her whole presence is RIPE, ALIVE.

She clears some of the debris, revealing SPIKE. He, in
contrast to his mate, is scared by fire and motionless.

Drusilla bends, wipes some ash from his brow. He responds,
unconscious - but alive.

                    DRUSILLA
          Don't worry, dear heart. I'll see
          that you get strong again...

CONTINUED

34 CONTINUED: 34

    She LIFTS SPIKE WITH ONE ARM. As if he were a toy. She
    obviously RELISHES every ounce of power.

                         DRUSILLA (cont'd)
              Like me.

    She smiles.

                                        BLACKOUT.

                         THE END

BUFFY THE VAMPIRE SLAYER

"Ted"

Written By

David Greenwalt & Joss Whedon

Directed By

Bruce Seth Green

SHOOTING SCRIPT

October 28, 1997 (FULL BLUE)
Ocotber 29, 1997 (FULL PINK)

BUFFY THE VAMPIRE SLAYER

"Ted"

CAST LIST

BUFFY SUMMERS........................... Sarah Michelle Gellar
XANDER HARRIS.......................... Nicholas Brendon
RUPERT GILES.......................... Anthony S. Head
WILLOW ROSENBERG....................... Alyson Hannigan
CORDELIA CHASE......................... Charisma Carpenter
ANGEL................................. David Boreanaz

JOYCE SUMMERS........................*Kristine Sutherland
JENNY CALENDAR.......................*Robia La Morte
TED BUCHANAN.........................*John Ritter
NEAL.................................*Ken Thorley
DETECTIVE STEIN......................*James G. MacDonald
VAMPIRE..............................

BUFFY THE VAMPIRE SLAYER

"Ted"

SET LIST

INTERIORS

SUNNYDALE HIGH SCHOOL
    HALL
        HALL OUTSIDE ASSISTANT PRINCIPAL'S OFFICE
    COMPUTER LAB
    LOUNGE
    LIBRARY
    SCIENCE LAB

BUFFY'S HOUSE
    BUFFY'S BEDROOM
    DINING ROOM\FOYER\HALL
    KITCHEN
    STAIRS
    FRONT PORCH
    UPSTAIRS HALL

ANGEL'S APARTMENT
LORRIN SOFTWARE
POLICE STATION
    INTERROGATION ROOM

CAR
TED'S HOUSE
    MACHINE SHOP
    TED'S BASEMENT

EXTERIORS

SUNNYDALE HIGH SCHOOL (STOCK)
    SCHOOL QUAD

BUFFY'S HOUSE
STREET BY BUFFY'S HOUSE
PARK
MINIATURE GOLF COURSE

BUFFY THE VAMPIRE SLAYER

"Ted"

TEASER

1 EXT. STREET BY BUFFY'S HOUSE - NIGHT   1

BUFFY walks along the street with XANDER and WILLOW,
approaching her house. Will and Xander are in the middle of
a discussion. Buffy walks slightly apart, enjoying the night.

> XANDER
> You don't know what you're talking
> about.

> WILLOW
> Xander, he was obviously in charge.

> XANDER
> He was a puppet! She was using
> him.

> WILLOW
> He didn't seem like the type to
> let himself be used.

> XANDER
> Well, that was her genius. He
> never even knew he was playing
> second fiddle. Buffy.

> BUFFY
> Huh?

> XANDER
> Who do you think was the real
> power -- the Captain or Tenille?

> BUFFY
> Um... who are those people?

> XANDER
> The Captain and Tenille!
>   (off her blank look)
> Boy, **somebody** was raised in a
> culture-free environment.

> BUFFY
> I'm sorry, I was just --

> WILLOW
> Thinking?

CONTINUED

1 CONTINUED: 1

                         BUFFY
               Not thinking. Just having a lot
               of happy nonthoughts. I love it
               when things are quiet around here.

                         XANDER
               Yeah, with Spike and Drusilla out
               of the way we've really been
               riding the mellow and am I like
               jinxing the hell out of us by
               saying that?

                         BUFFY
               We'll let you off this time.

                         WILLOW
               So we're pretty sure there aren't
               any more Tarakan assassins coming
               our way?

                         BUFFY
               Angel's sources say the contract
               is off.

                         XANDER
               How is Angel? Pretend I care.

                         BUFFY
               He's getting better.

                         WILLOW
               And you're loving playing
               nursemaid.

                         BUFFY
               Oh yeah.

                         XANDER
               So it's better than playing
               naughty stewardess?

                         BUFFY
               Xander...

She steps onto the porch, pulls out her keys. As Xander and
Willow step up behind her, Willow turns to Xander.

                         WILLOW
               I'm just saying, if Tenille was in
               charge, **she** would have had the
               little captain hat.

Buffy puts the key to the lock -- and the door swings open.
She stops, perturbed.

                                                        CONTINUED

1 CONTINUED: (2)   1

                     BUFFY
        Wait here.

Xander and Willow hand back as she eneters.

A INT. BUFFY'S FOYER - CONTINUOUS - NIGHT   1A

Buffy steps in, looks around. The house is dark. She pulls
a stake out, heads toward the living room.

ANGLE: XANDER AND WILLOW

Outside, wary.

ANGLE: BUFFY

Heads toward the dining room.

From the kitchen comes her mom's voice:

                     JOYCE (O.S.)
     No!

And a CRASH.

Buffy runs.

                     JOYCE (cont'd; O.S.)
     What are you...? Don't... oh...

2 INT. BUFFY'S HOUSE - KITCHEN - NIGHT   2

Dark, moonlit. Buffy bursts in.

                     BUFFY
     Get the hell away from my --

Buffy sees JOYCE, wrapped in a deep romantic kiss with TED
BUCHANAN, handsome and athletic, a born salesman. On the
counter near them, a wine bottle and one half full wine
glass.

                     BUFFY (cont'd)
     -- mom?

Joyce and Ted break. Joyce steps away from Ted, looks at
Buffy who quickly hides the stake behind her back.

                     BUFFY (cont'd)
     I thought I heard...

                     JOYCE
     I broke a wine glass. So, you're
     home early...

CONTINUED

Ted smiles, comfortably at ease -- unlike Joyce.

                    TED
          Hi.

                    BUFFY
          Hi.

                    JOYCE
          Oh, uh, this is my daughter,
          Buffy. And Buffy, this is... this
          is Ted.

                                        BLACK OUT.

                    END OF TEASER

ACT ONE

3   EXT./INT. BUFFY'S HOUSE - KITCHEN - NIGHT   3

A little later. The lights are on. In b.g. Xander and
Willow watch Ted cook mini-pizzas in a pan. In f.g., out of
their earshot, Joyce dumps the broken wine glass from the
dust pan into the trash, Buffy next to her.

                    BUFFY
          So all these late nights at the
          gallery, I gather you were   *
          cataloguing more than art.

                    JOYCE
          Well... I've been looking for the
          right moment to introduce you two.
          He's a wonderful man.

Joyce glances back at Ted, obvious affection in her eyes.

                    BUFFY
          How'd you meet?

                    JOYCE
          He sells computer software, he
          revamped my entire system at the
          gallery. Freed up a lot of my
          time.

                    BUFFY
          To meet new people. And smootch
          them in my kitchen.   *

                    JOYCE
          You weren't supposed to see that.

ANGLE - TED, XANDER & WILLOW AT STOVE

Xander devours a mini-pizza as Ted pulls more from the oven
and puts them in a pan.

                    WILLOW
          I like my new nine-gig hard   *
          drive...

                    TED
          But you don't love it, cause
          without the DMA upgrades your   *
          computer's really only half a
          rocket ship.

                                              CONTINUED

3 CONTINUED: 3

                         WILLOW
          Yeah. But who can afford the
          upgrades?

                         TED
          You can. I get the demos for
          free. I don't see why I shouldn't
          give them to you for the same
          price.
                    (hands her his card)
          Any friend of Buffy's...

Willow's eyes light up and she makes a high squeaking sound.

                         TED (cont'd)
          What?

                         XANDER
                    (mouth full of pizza)
          That's the sound she makes when
          she's speechless with geeker joy.
          Can I just say this is the finest
          pizza ever on God's green earth.
          What's your secret?

He turns back to the pan, taking it and bringing it over to
the island, dumping the pizzas on a plate.

                         TED
          After you bake it you fry it in
          herbs and olive oil. And you
          gotta use a cast iron skillet. No
          room for compromise there.

                         XANDER
          You gotta market these. I mean
          people would pay like two, three
          hundred dollars apiece.

Ted smiles, dishes up another pizza, carries it to:

BUFFY AND JOYCE

                         TED
                    (to Buffy)
          Hungry?

                         BUFFY
          No thanks.

He sets the plate down.

                         TED
          Buffy I want to apologize. That
          wasn't how I wanted us to meet.
                    (more)

                                                           CONTINUED

3 CONTINUED: (2)   3

                        TED (cont'd)
            I wanted it to be... perfect. I'm
            very fond of your mother, I guess
            that's pretty obvious...

Ted picks up a FRAMED PHOTO of Buffy and her Mom on the
counter. A loving mother daughter deal, <u>mostly headshot</u>.

                        TED (cont'd)
            ...I know you're the most
            important thing in her life and,
            well, gosh that makes you pretty
            important to me, too.

                        JOYCE
            I really want you to be okay with
            this, Buffy.

Ted wraps his arm around Joyce:

                        TED
            Beg to differ...
                    (to Buffy)
            ... <u>we</u> really want you to be okay
            with this.

                        BUFFY
            I'm okay.

                        JOYCE
            You are?

                        BUFFY
            I am.

Buffy smiles.

                                        SMASH CUT TO:

4 EXT. PARK - NIGHT   4

A VAMPIRE

Flies back and smashes into a picnic table, breaking it.

BUFFY

Charges. Grabbing a metal trash can lid en route. The
stunned vampire puts up his hands as Buffy begins beating him
over the head with the lid.

                                                CONTINUED

4   CONTINUED: 4

ANGLE: GILES

Watching Buffy's mayhem nearby. Mostly we HEAR (rather than
see) the carnage she is inflicting. GILES is concerned about
the level of her furor.

                    GILES
          Uh, Buffy... I believe he's...
                (that must have hurt)
          ...ahhh... it's staking time,
          really. Don't you think?

BUFFY

Hurls the trash can lid aside, raises a stake high in the
air. Stakes the vamp. She straightens up, breathing hard
and Giles joins her.

                    BUFFY
                (looking around)
          Any others?

                    GILES
          For their sakes I certainly hope
          not.

                    BUFFY
          What? I kill vampires, that's my
          job.

                    GILES
          True, although usually you don't
          beat them to quite such a bloody
          pulp beforehand. Everything all
          right?

                    BUFFY
          Everything's fine.
                (looking around)
          I killed one here Wednesday, why
          are they hanging at the park?

                    GILES
          They're scattered, you know.
          Their leaders are gone and with
          any luck dead. In times of crisis
          they will always return to the
          easiest feeding grounds.

                    BUFFY
                (grouchy)
          Vampires are creeps.

                                            CONTINUED

4 CONTINUED: (2)   4

                    GILES
               (duh)
          Yes, that's why one slays them.

                    BUFFY
          People are perfectly happy,
          getting along, then vampires come
          in and they run around and they
          kill people and they take over
          your whole house and they make
          these stupid little pizzas and
          everyone's like "ooh, wow"...

                    GILES
          Uh, Buffy, I believe the subtext
          here is rapidly becoming text.
          Are you sure there's nothing you
          wish to share with me?

                    BUFFY
          Forget about it. I'm fine.
               (hopefully)
          You think there'll be any more
          vampires? I can wait...

5 INT. SCHOOL HALL/LOUNGE - DAY   5

     As the bell rings and the hall fills, Buffy, Willow and
     Xander exit the classroom and head to the lounge.

                    BUFFY
          Xander, if you say one more word
          about it, things will become dire.

                    XANDER
          Did you even bother to taste 'em?
          Noooo. Well I did and I'm here to
          tell you, those mini pizzas have
          changed my life. Ted is the
          master chef.

                    BUFFY
          So? He's a great cook. What does
          that tell you about a person?

                    XANDER
          Everything.

                    WILLOW
          You don't like him.

                                            CONTINUED

5 CONTINUED: 5

                         BUFFY
              I don't know him.
                    (with disdain)
              I mean so far all I see is someone
              who apparently has a good job,
              seems nice and polite, my mom
              really likes him...

                         XANDER
                    (all dramatical)
              What kind of a monster is he!?

                         BUFFY
              I'm telling you, there's just
              something a little too clean about
              this clown.

                         WILLOW
                    (amused)
              He's a clean clown!
                    (off their looks)
              I have my own fun...

                         XANDER
              Buff, you're lacking evidence. I
              think we're maybe into Sigmund
              Freud territory.

                         WILLOW
              He has a point. Separation
              anxiety, the mother figure being
              taken away, conflict with the
              father figure...

                         BUFFY
              He's not my father figure!

                         XANDER
              Having issues much?

                         BUFFY
              I am not!

Xander points, with a mock-childish dance.

                         XANDER
              You've got parental issues, you've
              got parental issues.

                         WILLOW
              Xander...

                                                    CONTINUED

5 CONTINUED: (2)   5

                    XANDER
          Freud would have said the exact
          same thing. Except he might not
          have done the little dance.

                    BUFFY
          I admit it's weird -- seeing my
          mother frenching a guy is
          definitely a ticket to
          therapyland. But it's more than
          that. I'm pretty good at sensing
          what's going on around me...

Unbeknownst to Buffy, Ted is moving up behind her.

                    BUFFY (cont'd)
          ...and I know that something's
          wrong with this Ted.

                    XANDER
          Ted!

                    BUFFY
          Yeah, Ted. Who did you think I
          was --

                    XANDER
          Hi, Ted! Ted who's here.

Buffy spins, sees.

                    TED.
          Hello, kids.

                    BUFFY
          What are you doing here?

                    TED
          I'm updating the software in the
          guidance office -- which reminds
          me...

He hands Willow some computer disks.

                    TED (cont'd)
          ...your upgrades.   *

                    WILLOW
          Ohh, what a day! Thank you.

                    TED
          Think nothing of it. Buffy, you
          like miniature golf?

                                             CONTINUED

5 CONTINUED: (3)   5

                         XANDER
               Who doesn't?

                         TED
               Your mother and I were thinking,
               maybe this Saturday we could drag
               the three of you out to the
               course? Spend some time swinging
               the iron with the stuffy old
               people?

                         BUFFY
               Well, I guess...

                         TED
               I'm making a picnic basket...

                         XANDER
               Mini-pizzas?

                         TED
               And cookies.

                         BUFFY
               You know, I wish we could but
               Saturday we have that thing.

                         WILLOW
               Oh, that thing.
                    (to Xander)
               That thing.

                         XANDER
               Hey, we can do that thing anytime.
               I'm tired of that thing. We're on!

          Ted smiles.

6 INT. COMPUTER LAB - DAY   6

          JENNY is alone, clearing up. Giles enters, hesitantly.

                         GILES
               Hello, Jenny.

                         JENNY
               Rupert. Hi.

                         GILES
               A couple crates of your textbooks
               were dropped off at the library.
               Do you want me to hold on to them?

                                                              CONTINUED

6 CONTINUED: 6

                    JENNY
          Yeah, that's fine. I'll send the
          kids by to pick them up.

                    GILES
          Right. Good.

After an awkward beat, he starts out.

                    JENNY
          That was a pretty flimsy excuse
          for coming to see me.

                    GILES
               (stops)
          You should hear the ones I threw
          out.

He comes back in.

                    GILES (cont'd)
          I wanted to see how you were doing.

                    JENNY
          I'm doing pretty good, actually.
          I've stayed out of mortal danger
          for three whole weeks. I could
          get used to it. Still don't sleep
          too well, though.

                    GILES
          Of course. Well, you need time.

                    JENNY
          Or possibly space. Rupert, I know
          you're concerned, but having you
          constantly poking around making
          puppy dog eyes at me and wondering
          if I'm okay... you make me feel
          bad that I don't feel better. I
          don't want that responsibility.

                    GILES
          I'm sorry. I certainly don't mean
          to make dog eyes at you. I'm
          just --

                    JENNY
          Worried, I know.

                    GILES
          I shouldn't have bothered you.

                                                    CONTINUED

6 CONTINUED: (2)   6

He leaves. Jenny looks after him, obviously unsatisfied with
the whole exchange.

7 INT. ANGEL'S APT. - NIGHT   7

It's dark and romantic. Buffy changes the bandage on ANGEL'S
wounded hand, wrapping it quickly and neatly.

                    BUFFY
          So Mom's like, "Do you think Ted
          will like this" and, "That's Ted's
          favorite show," and "Ted's
          teaching me computers" and "Ted
          said the funniest thing," and I'm
          like, "that's great, Mom,". And
          then she said I was being
          sarcastic, which I was, but I'm
          sorry if I don't want to talk
          about Ted all the time.

                    ANGEL
          So you'll be talking about
          something else at some point?

                    BUFFY
          I'm sorry. It's just, I have so
          much to deal with, I don't need
          some new guy in my life right now.

                    ANGEL
          No, but maybe your mom does.

Buffy looks a little sheepish, says mock-sullenly:

                    BUFFY
          Oh, sure, if you're gonna use
          wisdom...

                    ANGEL
               (smiles)
          Loneliness is about the scariest
          thing there is.

                    BUFFY
          Okay, fine, so Mom needs a guy.
          Why does it have to be Ted?

                    ANGEL
          You have somebody else in mind?
          There's a guy out there that would
          satisfy you?

                    BUFFY
          Well... Dad... Okay, that's not
          gonna happen. Reality check.
               (more)

                                                    CONTINUED

7 CONTINUED: 7

                        BUFFY (cont'd)
             I'll give Ted a chance. I'll play
             mini golf. I'll smile and curtsey
             and be the dutiful daughter.
                       (beat)
             Do I have to like him?

                        ANGEL
             Kiss me.

                        BUFFY
             Oh, finally something I **wanna** do.

So she does.

8 EXT. MINIATURE GOLF COURSE - DAY   8

Buffy, Ted, Joyce, Xander and willow, clubs in hand, stand
before:

                        XANDER
             The dreaded par five cuckoo clock.   *
             So many came, so few conquered.

Xander addresses his ball. Joyce turns to Ted.

                        JOYCE
             That picnic was delicious. You
             know how rare it is to find a man
             who cooks?

                        TED
             I know I've been looking a long
             time for one.

Joyce laughs. Ted winks at Buffy. Buffy smiles, trying.

                        TED (cont'd)
             So Buffy, I'm sure the boys are
             lined up around the block trying
             to get a date with you.

                        BUFFY
             Not really.

                        WILLOW
             Oh they are but she's only
             interested in... uh... her
             studies. Book-cracker Buffy, it's
             kind of her nick name.

Willow moves to take her shot.

                                                        CONTINUED

8 CONTINUED: 8

                          TED
              Glad to hear that. I bet that
              means your grades'll be picking up
              soon.

                          BUFFY
              My grades?

Ted moves to shoot. Buffy moves to Joyce.

                          BUFFY (cont'd)
              How does he know about my grades?

                          JOYCE
              I told him. He wants to know all
              about you. He's concerned, that's
              a good thing.
                      (sees Ted shoot)
              Nice shot, Ted!

                          TED
              Thanks, Joycee.

Joyce prepares to take her swing. Ted holds her arms from
behind.

                          TED (cont'd)
              Steady swing, lead to the right.

Buffy watches her mother and Ted hit the ball together.

                          TED (cont'd)
              Perfect.

                          JOYCE
              Thanks to you.

Ted chuckles. Off Buffy, not loving this guy.

ANGLE - ANOTHER HOLE - LATER

This is one of those holes where you hit the ball in a little
castle or something and it rolls down onto a turf on a lower
level not visible from the tee.

Ted, Joyce, Willow and Xander watch as Buffy swings.

                          TED
              Eye on the ball... watch those
              elbows...

Her ball goes wild into some bushes.

                                                      CONTINUED

8 CONTINUED: (2)   8

                    TED (cont'd)
          Bad luck, little lady.

                    JOYCE
          We won't count it.

                                                  CONTINUED

8 CONTINUED: (3)   8

                    TED
          We won't?

                    JOYCE
          Well, it's just miniature golf.

                    TED
          It is, but the rules are the
          rules. What we teach her is what
          she takes into the world when
          we're not there, whether it's at
          school or an unchaperoned party...

Ted looks at Buffy, smiles.

                    TED (cont'd)
          I don't mean to overstep my
          bounds, this is between you and
          your mother. I just think right
          is right.

Buffy looks to her mother.

                    JOYCE
          He has a point...

                    BUFFY
               (not what she wanted
                to hear)
          Yah. I'll just go hit from the
          rough.

Buffy disappears into the bushes.

ANGLE - THE BUSHES - BUFFY LOOKS AROUND

No one can see her. She picks up her ball, walks to the
turf, drops it near the hole and kicks it in, calling back
over her shoulder:

                    BUFFY (cont'd)
          Hey, how 'bout that, I got a hole
          in two.

                    TED (O.S.)
          Beg to differ.

Buffy whirls around. Ted is standing right next to her.

                    BUFFY
          Okay, so fine my score or
          whatever...

                                                    CONTINUED

8 CONTINUED: (4)   8

                    TED
          I think you're missing the point
          here, little lady...

Ted starts tapping the golf club against his shoe. Creepy
like. Although he's still the friendly salesman, we get our
first glimpse into his psycho soul:

                    TED (cont'd)
          Right is right. Wrong is wrong.
          Why don't people see that?

                    BUFFY
          It's just a game.

                    TED
          Right. It's just a game. DO your
          own thing...

He takes step closer, the golf club hitting his leg harder
and faster.

                    TED (cont'd)
          Well I'm not wired that way. I'm
          here to tell you it is not a game
          and it does count and I don't
          stand for that kind of malarkey in
          my house.

                    BUFFY
          Then I guess it's a good thing I'm
          not in your house.

                    TED
          Do you want me to slap that smart
          ass mouth of yours?

Buffy reacts as Joyce, Willow, Xander come into view. And
the nice guy smile comes back to Ted's face.

                    TED (cont'd)
          Who's up for dessert? I made
          chocolate chip cookies.

Ted pulls out a big baggie of cookies.

                    XANDER
          Yum, me!

                    WILLOW
          Cookies.

                                        CONTINUED

8   CONTINUED: (5)   8

                          TED
              I made too many, so you guys are
              gonna have to take some home...

Buffy takes a step back, watching this cobra as the people
she cares most about gather innocently around him for cookies.

                          JOYCE
              Oh, you have to try one of these,
              Buffy, they're really good.

Off Buffy,

                                        BLACK OUT.

                    END OF ACT ONE

ACT TWO

9   EXT. BUFFY'S HOUSE - DAY - ESTABLISHING   9

10 INT. BUFFY'S HOUSE - KITCHEN - DAY   10

Joyce hums a little tune to herself as she sets out juice and
sticky buns. Buffy enters in a bad mood from lack of sleep
and Ted terror. Avid fans may note the absence of the framed
photo of Buffy and Joyce.

                    JOYCE
          Good morning sunshine.

                    BUFFY
          Hi.

                    JOYCE
          I've got juice. I've got sticky
          buns. Don't they smell good?

Buffy tears off a tiny piece o' bun.

                    JOYCE (cont'd)
          Ted made them.

Buffy puts the piece back down.

                    JOYCE (cont'd)
          What?

                    BUFFY
          I'd just like to eat something
          around here that Ted didn't make.

                    JOYCE
          What kind of attitude is that?

                    BUFFY
          Look, Mom, I know you think he's
          great and all but --

                    JOYCE
          He's gone out of his way to be
          nice to you and you couldn't find
          two words to say to him on
          Saturday. Now I don't expect you
          to love him right away like I do,
          but I do expect you to treat him
          decently.

                    BUFFY
          You... love him?

                                              CONTINUED

10 CONTINUED: 10

                         JOYCE
                    (beat)
               I don't know, that kind of slipped
               out... but I guess... it's not
               exactly like men beat down the
               door when you're a...

                         BUFFY
               ...single parent.

                         JOYCE
               I would never have anything to do
               with anyone who didn't care about
               you. But he does, I don't
               understand why you can't see that.

                         BUFFY
               He threatened me.

                         JOYCE
               What?

                         BUFFY
               He said he was going to slap my
               face.

Joyce looks at her daughter, concerned, then she does an odd
thing: she smiles.

                         JOYCE
               He never said any such thing. Ted
               told me what happened. He caught
               you cheating, didn't he.

                         BUFFY
               Yes. I kicked my ball in, so put
               me in jail, but he wigged --

                         JOYCE
               He didn't say anything about it in
               front of the others, did he.

                         BUFFY
               No, but --

                         JOYCE
               I think that was pretty decent of
               him.

Joyce begins eating little pieces of the sticky bun. Just a
little faster than a normal person would.

                                                      CONTINUED

10 CONTINUED: (2)   10

                    JOYCE (cont'd)
          Ted says we're just going to have
          to give you time to come around.
          Speaking of which, he's making
          dinner for us tonight, please be
          home promptly at six.

Joyce smiles at Buffy -- just a little too similar to Ted's
smile.

                    JOYCE (cont'd)
          These are so delicious.

11 EXT. SCHOOL - DAY - ESTABLISHING - STOCK   11

                    WILLOW (V.O.)
          What do you mean, check him out?

12 EXT. SCHOOL QUAD - DAY   12

Buffy is with her buds. They sit and eat cookies as they
talk to her.

                    BUFFY
          I mean, investigate him. Find out
          his secrets. You can do it, Will.
          Hack into his... life.

                    XANDER
          Can you say, "over-reaction'?

                    BUFFY
          Can you say, "sucking chest wound'?

                    WILLOW
          Buffy, it just seems like you **want**
          him to be corrupt or something.

                    BUFFY
          The man lost his senses over mini
          golf.

                    XANDER
          So he's uptight. Last I heard,
          that wasn't a slaying offense.
                    (off her look)
          Don't give me the look. I'm on
          your side. I'm just saying there
          are some things you have to accept.

                    BUFFY
          And I'm saying Ted ain't one of
          'em.

                                        CONTINUED

12 CONTINUED: 12

Cordy walks by.

                    XANDER
               Hey, Cordy. Nice outfit.

                    CORDELIA
                 (stopping)
               Oh, very funny.

                    XANDER
               Not really...

                    CORDELIA
               What are you saying?

                    XANDER
               "Nice outfit".

                    CORDELIA
               Why don't you just keep your mouth
               shut?

She takes off. Xander looks after her, not mad so much as
weary.

                    XANDER
               Would you guys excuse me for a
               second?

He goes after her. Willow watches him, brow furrowed.

                    WILLOW
               What's up with them?

ANGLE: XANDER AND CORDELIA

as he catches up to her.

                    CORDELIA
               What's wrong with you?

                    XANDER
               I gave you a compliment.

He's unusually calm and content with her.

                    CORDELIA
               In front of your friends! They're
               gonna know!

                    XANDER
               They're gonna know what?

                                                    CONTINUED

12 CONTINUED: (2)   12

                         CORDELIA
          Please. It's too traumatic for me
          even to say it.

                         XANDER
          That we kissed?

                         CORDELIA
          Gnegh!

                         XANDER
          I'm not gonna tell them and
          they're not gonna know. Not your
          friends, not my friends. You
          wanna go in the utility closet and
          make out?

                         CORDELIA
                   (furious)
          God! Is that all you ever think
          about?

Beat.

                         CORDELIA (cont'd)
          Okay.

They go.

ANGLE: BUFFY AND WILLOW

They are talking, so not see Xander and Cordy take off.

                         BUFFY
          Willow, I'm not wrong here. Ted   *
          has a problem with me. He acts   *
          like I'm in the way. And Mom's   *
          totally different since he's been
          around.

                         WILLOW
          Different like happy?

                         BUFFY
          Like Stepford. Will you help me?

                         WILLOW
          You know I will. What do you want
          me to look for?

                         BUFFY
          Let's start small. Where does he
          work?

13 INT. LORRIN SOFTWARE - DAY - BUFFY   13

She enters a room.   LORRIN SOFTWARE reads a large sign.

BUFFY'S POV - Rows of desks separated by dividers.   MEN and
WOMEN sell software over the phone.

[Avid fans of the show may note the remarkable similarity
between this telemarketing office and our own production
offices.]

WE PAN A CUBICLE and see NEAL, 30 to 50, death of a salesman.

                    NEAL
                 (on phone)
          ...it's a fantastic product, no
          p.c. should be without it... yes,
          it's a little pricey but... no, I
          don't think you're a feeble-minded
          moron... thanks for your time...

He hangs up and dials another number as we PAN to the next
cubicle and discover Ted, his neat desk completely bare
except for a picture frame, the back of the frame toward us.

                    TED
                 (on phone)
          No, Mrs. Lawndale, it's not an
          inexpensive piece of software. As
          a matter of fact it's a very
          expensive one. Which removes the
          risk of crashing your whole
          system. Of course if you prefer
          something cheap I can recommend...
                 (smiles)
          ...trust me, you won't be sorry.

Ted hangs up and gets up.

Buffy backs out of his line of sight as Ted moves to a large
SALES TOTE BOARD. He adds a check beneath his name (he has
ten times more sales than anyone else.)

                    TED (cont'd)
                 (to no one in
                  particular)
          Going to lunch.

He walks out. Buffy peers around the corner, watching him go.

                    NEAL (O.S.)
          You're new aren't you?

                                              CONTINUED

13 CONTINUED: 13

BUFFY is a little startled by Neal, getting a cup of water
nearby.

                    BUFFY
          Oh, uh...

                    NEAL
          I'm Neal.

                    BUFFY
          I'm Bu-linda. Just temping for
          the day.
                    (re: tote board)
          That guy's a salesman. Guess he's
          the one to beat around here.

                    NEAL
          Nobody beats the machine. The
          guy's a genius. Pure salesman.
          Knows everything about computers,
          never loses a client, never yells
          at the annoying clients... not
          that I do...

                    BUFFY
          I guess he's been doing this for
          a while.

                    NEAL
          He was here way before me - and
          he'll be here long after I'm gone.
          If I sound bitter, I am.

                    BUFFY
          Nobody likes an overachiever.
          Well, maybe he's got ex-wives and
          family to support.

                    NEAL
          All he's got is a girlfriend. I'm
          amazed he let her clutter up his
          desk.

Neal nods towards the picture on Ted's desk. Buffy looks --
CAMERA PUSHES in on the picture frame.

                    NEAL (cont'd)
          Thank god he's taking off for the
          wedding.

                    BUFFY
                    (evenly)
          The wedding?

                                              CONTINUED

13 CONTINUED: (2)   13

                         NEAL
               He's got it set for two months
               from now. Believe me, I'm
               counting the days.
                    (sees:)
               Uh oh, the uber-boss, back to the
               salt mines.

                                                    CONTINUED

13 CONTINUED: (3)   13

He moves off. Buffy moves to Ted's desk. Looks around,
casually pivots the picture so she can see it. It's the
picture from the kitchen but framed differently, showing
Joyce but not Buffy

Buffy picks up the frame, opens the back. Pulls out the
photo which is folded in half.

INSERT PHOTO - The half that shows Buffy is wrinkled and bent
backwards.

Buffy reacts, hurriedly puts the frame back together, gets
the hell out of there.

14 INT. BUFFY'S DINING ROOM - NIGHT   14

                    TED
          We thank you for the food we are
          about to receive...

Ted says grace. Joyce has her head obediently bowed. Buffy
watches Ted.

                    TED (cont'd)
          ...we ask that you bless this home
          and help those in it to be more
          productive, more considerate and...
                    (makes eye contact
                     with Buffy)
          ...more honest. Amen.

                    JOYCE
          Amen.

Ted dishes pasta Alfredo onto their plates.

                    TED
          Another great day at work. How
          was school, Buffy? Did ya' learn
          anything?

                    BUFFY
          Quite a bit.

                    TED
          Good for you.
                    (re: food)
          Well Joycee, what do ya' think?

                    JOYCE
          I think every home should have
          someone like you. It's fantastic.
                    (to Buffy)
          Don't you think?

                                                        CONTINUED

14 CONTINUED: 14

Buffy's just pushing her fork around her plate.

                    BUFFY
          It... looks pretty good.

                    TED
          Well you know, little lady, it's
          not just for looks, it's for
          building strong bodies.
                    (smiles)

                    JOYCE
                    (eat some)
          Honey...

Buffy slowly brings a forkful towards her mouth. But instead
of eating:

                    BUFFY
          Are you guys engaged?

                    JOYCE
          What? Goodness, no, what gave you
          that idea?

                    TED
          Now Joycee, let me handle this.
          Your mother and I are taking
          things one step at a time, but if
          things go the way I hope someday
          soon I just might ask her to tie
          the knot. How would you feel
          about that?

Buffy looks from Ted to her mother, not wanting to answer.

                    TED (cont'd)
          It's okay to have your feelings,
          Buffy. And it's okay to express
          them.

                    BUFFY
          I'd feel like killing myself.

                    JOYCE
          Buffy!

                    TED
          No, no, I told her to be honest.
                    (to Buffy)
          Sweetheart, you should try and get
          used to me cause you know what?
          I'm not going anywhere.

                                                        CONTINUED

14 CONTINUED: (2)   14

Beat.

                    BUFFY
           May I be excused?

                    JOYCE
           You can go to your room, young
           lady, that's what you can do.

Buffy gets up, heads upstairs.

                    JOYCE (cont'd)
           Ted, I'm so embarrassed. I don't
           know what's wrong with her.

                    TED
           You don't get to be salesman of
           the year by giving up after a
           couple of rejections. She'll come
           around, and a little birdy's
           telling me it's going to be sooner
           rather than later.

He puts a comforting hand on Joyce's forearm. She gains a
little strength from his unrelenting confidence.

                    JOYCE
           Where did you come from?

                    TED
           Straight from the factory. And we
           pass those savings on to you.

She laughs, comforted.

15 EXT. PARK - NIGHT   15

Buffy sits on a swing, looking into the night.

Nothing's going on. She looks behind her, around.

                    BUFFY
           Vampires...
                ("here kitty")
           Here, vampires...

Nothing doing. She gets up and goes.

16 INT. BUFFY'S BEDROOM - NIGHT   16

Buffy slips in the window. Oh yeah, it's dark and creepy in
here and that's why it takes a moment for her to spot Ted
leaning against her vanity.

                    BUFFY
               What are you doing?

As usual, Ted is his jovial good guy self.

                    TED
               Your mother said go to your room,
               Buffy. I think we both know she
               didn't mean climb out your window
               and go gallivanting about town.

                    BUFFY
               First of all, this is my room.
               Second of all --

She stops, seeing her vanity drawers open, stakes and holy
water out, along with her journal which is open next to Ted.

                    BUFFY (cont'd)
               -- have you been going through my
               things?

                    TED
               Yes I have.

                    BUFFY
               How dare you. That's my personal
               property. How dare you!

                    TED
               I don't see how it's any different
               than you snooping around my
               office. Do you?

Buffy reacts. Ted picks up her journal.

                    TED (cont'd)
               What exactly is a vampire slayer?

                    BUFFY
               That's none of your business.

                    TED
               Beg to differ, little lady.
               Everything you do is nothing but
               my business from now on.

                                        CONTINUED

.6 CONTINUED: 16

                         BUFFY
            You better get out of here. Now.

Ted moves close to her, invading her space.

                         TED
            Or what. You'll "slay" me? I'm
            real, I'm not some goblin you made
            up in your diary. The
            psychiatrists have a word for this
            kind of thing...
                    (re: journal)
            ...delusional. From no on you
            are going to do what I say when I
            say or I show this to your mother
            and you spend your best dating
            years behind the walls of a mental
            institution. Your mother and I
            are going to be happy. You're not
            getting in the way of that. Sleep
            tight.

After a tense beat he turns to go, journal in hand. She
grabs his arm.

                         BUFFY
            That's mine and you're not leaving
            this room with it.

                         TED
            Take your hand off me.

                         BUFFY
            No.

A stand-off. Until he suddenly slaps her face!

                         BUFFY (cont'd)
            Oh. I was so hoping you'd do that.

And she hauls off and smashes him in the face. About as hard
as a Slayer can. He slams back into the door, knocking it
open into the hall.

And he comes for her, fast and vicious.

He swings, hits her hard -- Arnold Schwarzeneggar hard.
She's stunned. He grabs her by the hair, drags her towards
the door. She knees him, preferably in the groin. Then she
hits him hard, once, twice, as her mother appears in the
hallway --

                         JOYCE
            Buffy! Stop it!

                                                    CONTINUED

16 CONTINUED: (2)   16

Buffy spin kicks him to the head and sends him flying out the
door.

17 INT. BUFFY'S HOUSE - STAIRS - NIGHT   17

Ted caroms off the wall, loses his footing and tumbles head
over heels down the stairs.

His head lands at the bottom with a sharp and nasty THUNK.

Buffy stands at the top of the stairs, breathing hard. Joyce
tears past her down the stairs, nearly falling herself and
kneels next to Ted.

                         JOYCE
              Ted... Ted!

She puts her hand on his chest, desperate. She puts her ear
to his mouth, listening. She grabs for a pulse. There is
none.

Joyce looks up at her daughter.

                         JOYCE (cont'd)
              You... you killed him.

Off Buffy,

                                              BLACK OUT.

                         END OF ACT TWO

ACT THREE

18   INT. BUFFY'S HOUSE - A HALF HOUR LATER - NIGHT   18

ANGLE: TED

As the black plastic bag is zipped over his face.

18A   EXT/ BUFFY'S HOUSE - CONTINUOUS - NIGHT   18A

The area is filled with the usual crime scene professionals.

Buffy sits on the porch, in silent shock. Joyce stands
looking into the foyer, away from Buffy, as Ted's body is
carried out by two morgue guys. Moving past them is
DETECTIVE STEIN. He approaches Joyce.

                    STEIN
          Ma'am, I'm Detective Stein... I'm
          sorry but I need to ask you a few
          things... Your relationship with
          the deceased?

                    JOYCE
          We were... um, seeing each other.

                    STEIN
          Can you tell me what happened?

It's a beat before she answers.

                    JOYCE
          He fell. Down the stairs. He
          fell.

                    STEIN
          I see. Did he slip, do you know
          what made him fall?

                    BUFFY
          I hit him.

She is still sitting, staring. They turn to look at her. It
is suddenly very quiet in here.

                    BUFFY (cont'd)
          I hit him.

19   INT. POLICE STATION - NIGHT   19

The place is a bustle of activity, even this late. Joyce
Summers sits on a bench by herself, waiting. Quiet.

20 INT. INTERROGATION ROOM - CONTINUOUS - NIGHT   20

Detective Stein sits with Buffy. His tone is intimate and
comforting, not interrogational. She speaks quietly,
intensely.

                    BUFFY
          He was in my room... we got into
          an argument...

                    STEIN
          About what?

                    BUFFY
          He... um, he'd been --

                    STEIN
          Was this the first time you two
          had had an argument?

                    BUFFY
               (after a beat)
          No. He threatened me. He said he
          would slap me...

                    STEIN
          That was tonight?

                    BUFFY
          No... but he had my diary and I
          tried to take it back and... and
          then he hit me.

                    STEIN
          Where?

She points to her cheek.

                    STEIN (cont'd)
          It doesn't look like he hit you
          very hard.

                    BUFFY
               (staring at him)
          I don't bruise easily.

                    STEIN
          So you've been hit before?

                    BUFFY
          Yes...

                    STEIN
          But Ted never hit you.

                                        CONTINUED

20 CONTINUED: 20

                              BUFFY
                    I told you, he --

                              STEIN
                     -- Before tonight. Never hit you
                    before tonight.

                              BUFFY
                         (more confused than
                         angry)
                    What do you want? I told you what
                    happened. I didn't mean to...

                              STEIN
                    I believe you. Things got out of
                    hand. He's a big guy.

As Buffy stares off, thinking...

                              JOYCE (V.O.)
                    Are you charging her with
                    something?

21 INT. POLICE STATION - LATER - NIGHT   21

He leans on his desk, Joyce standing before him.

                              STEIN
                    We're not bringing anything up
                    against your daughter right now.
                    She says Mr. Buchanan struck her
                    and if that's the case... anyway
                    we're gonna examine it further.
                    Right now I think you should just
                    take her home and the two of you
                    try to get some rest.

Off her look --

21A EXT. STREET - NIGHT   21A   *

Joyce's car drives by.   *

22 INT. CAR - NIGHT   22

Joyce and Buffy sit side by side. Silent. Buffy almost
tries to say something to her mother, but either thinks
better of it or can't think of anything to say.

Joyce never looks at her.

23 INT. SCHOOL - DAY   23

    Buffy enters the hall, obviously not after a great night's
    sleep. She passes a whispering gaggle of girls -- who nudge
    each other and hush up as she passes.

                                                     CONTINUED

23 CONTINUED: 23

Further down the hall and she passes two teachers who stare
at her unabashedly. She moves into:

24 INT. LOUNGE - CONTINUOUS - DAY   24

Where Xander and Willow accost her.

                    XANDER
          Buffy! Are you okay?

                    WILLOW
          How come you're here?

                    BUFFY
          I couldn't stay home... Mom won't
          even look at me.

They sit at one of the tables.

                    WILLOW
          What happened? Unless you don't
          want to talk about it...

                    BUFFY
          We had a fight. I lost my temper,
          really let him have it.

                    WILLOW
          The papers said he fell.

                    BUFFY
          He fell. Hard.

                    XANDER
          Well, what was he?

                    BUFFY
          What?

                    XANDER
          What was he? Demon? Giant bug?
          Some kind of dark god with the
          secrets of nouvelle cuisine? I
          mean, we are talking creature
          feature here, right?

Buffy doesn't answer.

                    XANDER (cont'd)
          Oh, man...

                    WILLOW
          But, I'm sure it wasn't your
          fault. He started it!

                                                    CONTINUED

24 CONTINUED: 24

                              BUFFY
                    Yeah, that defense only works in
                    six-year-old court, Will.

                              XANDER
                    Court? Are you -- are they
                    charging you with something?

                              BUFFY
                    I don't know. Not yet. But...
                    He was a guy. He was a weird,
                    sleazy guy but he was a person and
                    I killed him.

                              WILLOW
                    Don't say that.

                              BUFFY
                    Why not? Everyone else is. And
                    it's the truth.

                              XANDER
                    It was an accident.

                              BUFFY
                    I'm the Slayer. I had no right to
                    hit him like that.

                              XANDER
                    Look, I don't know what happened
                    exactly, but I know you. You
                    would never hurt anyone
                    intentionally. You know, unless --

                              BUFFY
                    Unless what? They're dating my
                    Mom?
                         (stands)
                    I'm sorry, guys, I gotta be alone
                    for a while. I'll, um, I'll
                    just...

She can't think of anything. Turns and goes. They watch
her, distraught.

25 INT. HALL OUTSIDE ASSISTANT PRINCIPAL'S OFFICE - DAY   25

Buffy walks slowly down the hall. At the other end, Giles
emerges from the Assistant Principal's office. Sees Buffy
and crosses to her, stopping her some 15 feet from the
office.

                              GILES
                    Buffy. Are you all right?

                                                      CONTINUED

5 CONTINUED: 25

She shrugs.   *

                    GILES (cont'd)   *
          Stupid question. I'm sorry.   *
          Anything you need, of course, just   *
          ask.   *

Buffy sees the Assistant Principal (a large, stern woman)   *
step out and signal a waiting teacher to come in. (Another   *
teacher also waits).   *

                    BUFFY   *
          What's going on?   *

                    GILES   *
          You needn't worry about it.   *

Buffy steps forward to look.   *

                    GILES (cont'd)   *
          They were just asking questions --   *
          your record, your behavior...   *

                                                CONTINUED

25   CONTINUED: (2)   25

ANGLE: BUFFY'S POV INTO OFFICE

She sees the teacher shaking hands with Detective Stein, who
motions for her to sit down. The Assistant Principal hovers
nearby.

                    GILES (cont'd)
          Of course I told them you were --

But she takes off, unable to deal. Giles watches her,
unhappily.

26   INT. LIBRARY - AFTER SCHOOL - DAY   26

Giles crosses from the book cage and drops a bag of weapons
on the table. Willow sits at it, firing up the computer.
Cordy stands nearby, Xander pacing intensely.

                    XANDER
          Man, this is killing me! That
          bastard was up to something. I
          know it. if I could get my hands
          on him... earlier this week...

                    CORDELIA
          I thought you liked him.

                    XANDER
               (pointedly)
          I sometimes like things that are
          not good for me. Besides, no way
          no how does Buffy put the big hurt
          on an innocent man. Nice Uncle
          Ted was dirty.

                    WILLOW
          We gotta prove that somehow.
          Xander, you got a pen?

He goes for his back pack, digs.

                    XANDER
          If Buffy has to go to jail because
          of that creep, I'm gonna lose it.
          He's gotta be in there, Will.
          History of domestic violence,
          criminal record... ooh, cookies.

He pulls them out -- they are leftovers from the golf day --
as he hands Willow the pen. She starts to copy down a web
address.

                    CORDELIA
          I don't get it. Buffy's the
          Slayer, shouldn't she have...

                                                    CONTINUED

                    XANDER
          A license to kill?

He takes out a cookie. Eats.

                    CORDELIA
          Well, not for fun, but... I mean
          she's like this superman.
          Shouldn't there be different rules
          for her?

                    WILLOW
          Sure, in a fascist society.

                    CORDELIA
          Right! Why can't we have one of
          those?

                    WILLOW
          Buffy's not going to jail. It's
          not fair.

                    GILES
          Whatever the authorities are
          planning for her can't be much
          worse than what she's doing to
          herself. She took a human life.
          The guilt... it's pretty hard to
          bear and it won't go away soon.

                    CORDELIA
          Wow, yeah... I guess you'd know
          since you helped raise that demon
          that got that guy killed that time.

                    GILES
          Yes, do let's bring that up as
          often as possible.

He retreats to the book cage.

                    XANDER
                (eating another
                 cookie)
          So, Giles, you're taking over
          tonight?

                    GILES
          Buffy's in no shape to patrol.   *
          The least I can do is pick up the
          slack. Someone has to.

                    WILLOW
          Giles, you shouldn't go out there
          without the Slayer.

                                                    CONTINUED

26 CONTINUED: (2)   26

                         GILES
              Until Buffy regains her
              equilibrium, I'm afraid there is
              no Slayer.

                         CORDELIA
              If you need help...

                         GILES
              Buffy needs your help more than I.
              Continue investigating. Find out
              some more about Mr. Buchanan, if
              you can.

He shoulders his bag and starts out.

                         WILLOW
              Be careful.

                         GILES
              I will.

He's out the door. Cordy turns to Willow.

                         CORDELIA
              Are you sure it's a good idea for
              him to go out?

                         WILLOW
              Ted's got no criminal record I can
              find. Damn! The guy's like,
              citizen of the year!

                         XANDER
              Don't sweat it. Everything'll be
              fine.

                         WILLOW
              Don't sweat it?

He smiles, ruffles Willow's hair.

                         XANDER
              Yeah, cute buddy, we'll work it
              out. No worries.

                         CORDELIA
              What happened to "This is killing
              me?"

                         XANDER
              Worrying isn't gonna solve any
              problems.

                                                     CONTINUED

6 CONTINUED: (3)   26

The girls look at each other, confused by the radical tude
shift. Willow looks at Xander. He puts yet another cookie
in his mouth.

She reaches up. Breaks off half.

7 INT. BUFFY'S HOUSE - NIGHT   27

Joyce is in the kitchen, putting some old pots and
kitchenwares into a cardboard box. Buffy enters, tentatively.

                    BUFFY
          Can I help?

                    JOYCE
          It's done. I've been meaning to
          clean out this junk for months.

A beat. Neither of them knows how to scale this wall.

                    JOYCE (cont'd)
          Do you have... homework?

                    BUFFY
          I didn't mean to hurt him.

                    JOYCE
          I don't want to talk about this.

                    BUFFY
          Mom, you have to know --

                    JOYCE
          I can't. Not yet. Please, Buffy,
          just go to your room.

She takes the box and goes down to the cellar. Buffy waits,
then turns and goes towards her room.

8 INT. SCIENCE LAB - NIGHT   28

Willow is in full chemist mode, beakers abubblin'. Xander
hands her a solution. She puts it on a slide and looks at it
through a microscope.

                    WILLOW
          Okay...

                    XANDER
          What do we know?

                    WILLOW
          Apparently, the secret ingredient
          is not love.

                                                   CONTINUED

>   XANDER
>   What is it, then?

>   WILLOW
>   I'm not positive, but I think it's
>   Dematorin. It's like a
>   tranquilizer, keeps you all mellow
>   and compliant. And it shares a
>   few components with ecstasy.

>   XANDER
>   This is evidence. This is real
>   evidence that Ted was some kind of
>   crook. Buffy's cleared! Willow,
>   you're the best human ever. I
>   adore you.
>   (off her slightly
>   skeptical look)
>   That's the cookies talking, but
>   you rock.

Cordelia enters, holding a sheet of paper.

>   CORDELIA
>   Your search finally hit pay dirt.
>   Got some personal records,
>   marriage certificates, and an
>   address.

>   XANDER
>   Let's check it out. Get our
>   Slayer back on her feet before
>   somebody else gets hurt.

29 EXT. PARK - NIGHT   29

Giles waits for a sign of trouble. Someone appears near him
and he spins, holds up a cross.

Jenny looks at it, smiles wryly.

>   JENNY
>   I get that reaction from men all
>   the time.

>   GILES
>   Jenny! What are you doing here?

>   JENNY
>   I saw your car back there... I
>   wanted to apologize.

                                                    CONTINUED

29 CONTINUED: 29

                         GILES
            I don't think this is a good time
            to --

                         JENNY
            Please. Let me get this out. I
            was very harsh the other day. I
            know how bad you feel about
            putting me in danger before...

                         GILES
            Imagine how I must feel now.

He is looking behind her. She turns to see:

A vampire. Big fella.

30 INT. BUFFY'S BEDROOM - NIGHT   30

Buffy leans on the edge of her dresser, looking at nothing in
particular. Thinks she hears something, calls out softly:

                         BUFFY
            Mom?

But there is no reply. For a moment Buffy sinks back into
her depressed reverie, then:

                         BUFFY (cont'd)
            The hell with this.

She grabs her coat, throws it on as she moves to the window.
A quick glance at the hall and she tugs on the window to open
it. it won't budge. She looks more closely.

                         BUFFY (cont'd)
            She nailed it shut?

CLOSE ON: BUFFY

in profile, as she stares down at the window.

                         BUFFY
            Well, it's official. This day
            can't get any worse.

Ted's face comes into frame right beside her. Grinning.

                         TED
            Beg to differ...

                    END OF ACT THREE

ACT FOUR

31   INT. BUFFY'S BEDROOM - NIGHT - SECONDS LATER   31

Buffy backs up, confused and horrified.

                    BUFFY
          You... you died...

                    TED
          That's right, little lady. You
          killed me! Do we have something
          to say about that? Are we sorry?

Suspicion creeps into Buffy's gaze.

                    BUFFY
          What are you?

                    TED
          I'm a salesman! That's what you
          should have remembered. No matter
          how you put him down --

He backhands her so hard she flies halfway across the room --
slams into a wall.

                    TED (cont'd)
          -- a good salesman always bounces
          back.

32   EXT. PARK - NIGHT   32

The Vampire leaps on Giles, taking him to the ground. Giles
manages to hold off actual biting with his cross, but the guy
won't get off him.

Jenny looks around for a weapon --

                    GILES
          My bag!

She spots it on the ground, several feet away. She runs to
it, digs in it. Comes up with a crossbow.

Giles punches the Vamp, jarring him enough to roll free. He
pulls a stake from his coat but the vamp knocks it away.

Jenny stands, trying to take aim...

33   INT. BUFFY'S BEDROOM - NIGHT   33

Ted comes at Buffy and she kicks him hard. He staggers back
and she comes at him with a series of blows that would
cripple a normal man.

Which Ted is not, since he just smiles and grabs her by the
throat.

                    TED
          I had to shut down for a little
          while to get you off my back. You
          should have seen the intern's face
          when I got up off the table. It
          was a hoot. Fun's over, though.

His fingers tighten.

34   EXT. PARK - NIGHT   34

The Vampire grabs Giles, going in for the taste treat. Jenny
tries to get a bead --

ANGLE: JENNY'S POV

of the vampire's back. She's got a shot.

                    JENNY
          Say good night, big guy...

She fires.

Meanwhilst, the Vamp and Giles spin around in their
struggle -- and **the arrow hits Giles** in the side.

                    GILES
          AAAHHH!

                    JENNY
          Oh god! Oh no!

She scrambles to find another weapon, another arrow --

The Vampire lets go of Giles -- 'cause he's **laughing**.

With grim determination, Giles grabs the arrow (probably out
of frame) and pulls in from his side.

                    VAMPIRE
          TA-ha ha ha ha ha!!! Nice shot,
          lady.

Giles buries the arrow in the Vamp's heart. The Vamp's eyes
widen and he stops laughing for a moment. His last.

35 INT. BUFFY'S BEDROOM - NIGHT   35

Buffy is passing out from the pressure. Ted has her up
against her dresser, is still squeezing.

ANGLE: BUFFY'S HAND

searches and finds a nail file.

She swings and stabs his forearm. He backs off, grabbing his
arm. Buffy collapses to the floor gasping and looks up to
see:

CLOSE UP: THE CUT

It's not blood that trickles out. It looks suspiciously like
motor oil. And from within, there is a spark.

                    TED
          That wasn't playing fair, missy.
          You're gonna find --

We hear an electrical short and Ted's head snaps to the
right, a giant smile plastered on his face as he says:

                    TED (cont'd)
          Hell of a day! Day like this
          makes you feel 18 again!

And his head snaps back -

                    TED (cont'd)
          ... that I don't like being
          disobeyed.

Buffy can hardly speak through the strangling. But she
manages to whisper:

                    BUFFY
          How do you like... being hurt...?

He advances on her, pure murder in his eyes.

35A INT. KITCHEN - CONTINUOUS - NIGHT   35A

Joyce comes up from the cellar with an empty box. She KICKS
the door shut with her foot.

35B INT. BUFFY'S BEDROOM - CONTINUOUS - NIGHT   35B

This stops Ted. He turns and punches Buffy, knocking her
unconscious.

CONTINUED

35B CONTINUED: 35B

                              TED
               Don't worry about me and your mom.
               We're gonna be very happy.

He leaves the room, shutting the door behind him. We hear it
lock.

36 INT. MACHINE SHOP - NIGHT   36

The room is dark, empty, quiet. That is, until the brick
smashes through the window.

Xander reaches through and opens the door.

                    WILLOW (O.S.)
               Careful!

Cordy and Willow enter as he switches on the light.

The room is dusty, unused -- and kind of a mess. Computer
and machine parts litter the place.

                    XANDER
               Let's look around.

                    CORDELIA
               I'll take the back.

                    XANDER
               Check for cookies.
                    (off her look)
               For evidence.

                    WILLOW
                    (leafing through
                    documents)
               I count four marriage certificates.

                    XANDER
               Any divorce papers?

                    WILLOW
               Not a one.

                    XANDER
               So either our boy was a mormon,
               or...

                    WILLOW
               Whoah. 1957. Ted must have
               married young. Like, preschool
               young.

Cordy comes back in.

                    CORDELIA
               Nothing interesting. It doesn't
               look like anybody worked here, let
               alone lived here.

                                                      CONTINUED

36 CONTINUED: 36

                    XANDER
          Something's missing. This doesn't
          seem like Ted at all.

                    CORDELIA
          And that rug totally doesn't go
          with the rest of the decor.

Xander and Willow look at each other.

Xander pulls the corner of the rug up.

ANGLE: UNDER THE RUG

is a trapdoor.

37 INT. BUFFY'S HOUSE - NIGHT   37

Joyce is in the kitchen, busying herself. She hears
something behind her. Turns to say:

                    JOYCE
          Buffy, I'm sorry, I know you --

Ted is standing in the doorway.

Joyce freaks -- takes a stumbling step backwards, eyes wide,
unable to speak.

                    TED
          Joyce...

                    JOYCE
          Ted? Is it really... but you
          were...

                    TED
          I'm okay. I'm okay...

He crosses to her, takes her in his arms. She lets him hold
her a sec, then breaks free, looks at him.

                    JOYCE
          I don't understand this. You were
          dead.

                    TED
          They said I must have been dead
          for six minutes. They said any
          longer and there would have been
          brain damage.

                                        CONTINUED

37   CONTINUED: 37

                         JOYCE
              Why didn't anyone tell us?

                         TED
              Nobody knew! They took me to the
              morgue and I was unconscious for
              almost a day! An intern found me.
              It's a miracle, Joyce. A miracle.

                         JOYCE
              Oh, Ted...

                         TED
              I know...

                         JOYCE
              Oh my god, Buffy... Ted, I swear
              she never meant to hurt you, you
              have to believe me.

                         TED
              You don't have to worry about
              Buffy. You don't have to worry
              about anything. Daddy's here.

38   INT. TED'S BASEMENT - NIGHT   38

     The trapdoor opens, our three coming down concrete steps.

     What they find inside is a time capsule -- a perfect kitschy
     50's home set up inside a concrete bunker. There are even
     windows that look out onto concrete wall. it's spotless.
     It's creepy.

     ANGLE: A RECORD PLAYER

     As one innocuous 50's Jackie and Roy type album finishes and
     another drops down on top of it, starts PLAYING.

                         CORDELIA
              Feels just like home, if it's the
              50's and you're a psycho.

     The three look around. Xander finds a closet door behind a
     chest of drawers.

                         XANDER
              Whatdya got in the closet, Ted?

     He moves the chest and opens the door.

                                                          CONTINUED

38 CONTINUED: 38

ANGLE: XANDER FROM INSIDE CLOSET

He goes very still. Steely horror narrows his gaze and he
slams the door shut.

He starts out.

                    XANDER (cont'd)
               Let's go.

                    CORDELIA
               We need evidence --

                    XANDER
               We got it.

                    WILLOW
               What's in there?

                    XANDER
               His first four wives.

39 INT. BUFFY'S HOUSE - KITCHEN - NIGHT   39

                    TED
               You know what brought me back,
               Joyce? It was you. I couldn't go
               into that light -- I had to come
               back for you. I'm gonna make you
               so happy...

                    JOYCE
               You should sit down...

                    TED
               I feel fine. Never better.

                    JOYCE
               Ted, I think **I** should talk to
               Buffy first, before she sees you.
               I know she'll want to --

                    TED
                    (a little strident)
               Do we have to worry about Buffy
               right now? How about worrying
               about Teddy, he's the one that
               died.

                    JOYCE
               I'm sorry, I'm just... I don't
               know what to do.

                                                    CONTINUED

39 CONTINUED: 39

> TED
> (softly, taking her
> hands)
> Don't I always tell you what to
> do? I'm gonna make this right,
> and then you and I --

A sparking SOUND and his head whips to the side again --

> TED (cont'd)
> --want a little gravy with that? --

and he's back --

> TED (cont'd)
> -- can go away where no one will
> bother us again.

Okay, now Joyce is starting to get weirded.

> JOYCE
> Ted, I think you might want to
> rest for a while...

> TED
> I think you might want to stop
> telling me what to do. I don't
> take orders from women. I'm not
> wired that way.

40 INT. BUFFY'S BEDROOM - NIGHT   40

Buffy begins to stir. Turns, moaning, and coughs.

41 EXT. PARK - NIGHT   41

Jenny is kneeling, holding Giles.

> JENNY
> Oh, god, I'm so sorry...

> GILES
> I think I'm all right.

> JENNY
> You're just in shock --

> GILES
> No, really. It didn't go in that
> deep. The advantage of layers of
> tweed, I guess. Better than
> kevlar.

                                                        CONTINUED

41 CONTINUED: 41

                    JENNY
          We've still got to get you to a
          hospital.

                    GILES
          Yes.

They start to move --

                    GILES (cont'd)
          OW! Ow. Let's move slowly, shall
          we?

Still crazed by the whole deal, Jenny actually starts
laughing.

                    GILES (cont'd)
          What is it?

                    JENNY
          Some night, huh? You sure know
          how to woo a girl back, don't you.

                    GILES
               (cracks up too)
          Heh heh--owwwwww.

                    JENNY
          Hospital.

42 INT. BUFFY'S DINING ROOM - NIGHT   42

Joyce is walking into the dining room, Ted behind her. She
is pretending nothing's wrong. She is not the great
pretender.

                    JOYCE
          I think I could use a drink. To
          celebrate.

                    TED
          We should probably be hitting the
          road.

                    JOYCE
          Hitting the road?

                    TED
          You're gonna love the house. It's
          furnished just the way you like
          it. I spent a lot of --
               (more)

                                                    CONTINUED

42 CONTINUED: 42

                    TED (cont'd)
                    (spark)
            --**telling me what to do!**
                    (normal)
            -- time decorating.

There is the NOISE from upstairs of Buffy putting her
shoulder to her locked door.

                    JOYCE
            Well, then, I'd probably better
            pack.

                    TED
            I already have your clothes.
            They're your size, they're always
            your size. You left me once but
            I keep bringing you back. Husband
            and wife is forever. Forever.

43 INT. UPSTAIRS HALL - NIGHT   43

as the lock FLIES off the door, a still dazed Buffy pulling
the door open and stumbling out.

44 INT. BUFFY'S DINING ROOM\FOYER\HALL\KITCHEN - NIGHT   44

Ted heard that. He grabs Joyce.

                    TED
            Let's go.

She tries to break free --

                    JOYCE
            Ted, please, let go! Get OFF ME!

-- and succeeds, which kind of displeases him. He slams her
into a wall, knocking her unconscious.

                    TED
            Fine, then. I'll have to carry
            you.

A CREAK from the foyer makes him stop. He crosses into
there -- no one about. He moves quietly down the hall into
the kitchen. Turns to go in the dining room.

                    TED (cont'd)
            Come out, Buffy. I don't stand
            for this kind of malarkey in my
            house.

Buffy steps up behind him with a large cast iron skillet.
When she speaks, it is still a hoarse whisper.

                                                        CONTINUED

4 CONTINUED: 44

                    BUFFY
          Uncle Teddy...

He turns and she **homeruns** his face. He flies back, lands
hard.

                    BUFFY (cont'd)
          This house is mine.

CLOSE ON: TED

As he sits back up, enough of his face ripped away to reveal
the robot beneath.

He stands, Buffy taking a moment to register the creepiness
of his new face.

                    TED
          Buffy...

He's sparking badly, moving like a zombie, his voice now low
and mechanical --

-- Buffy brings the skillet back --

                    TED (cont'd)
          How about a nice game of Parcheesi?

-- and she takes him out. He falls hard, for the last time.

Off her look,

                                        DISSOLVE TO:

5 EXT. FRONT PORCH - DAY   45

Joyce and Buffy are shelling peas on the porch.

                    JOYCE
          You want to rent a movie tonight?

                    BUFFY
          That'd be fun.

                    JOYCE
          Just nothing with horror in it.
          Or romance. Or men.

                    BUFFY
          Sound like we're Thelma and
          Louising it again.

                                        CONTINUED

45 CONTINUED: 45

                        JOYCE
              Good call.
                    (beat)
              I still think he's gonna jump out
              at me. Especially after what the
              police found in his house, it's
              too horrible...

                        BUFFY
              He's not coming back, Mom.

                        JOYCE
              I wish I could be so sure.

                        BUFFY
              Trust me. he's on the scrap heap.
                    (covering)
              ...of life.

46 INT. SCHOOL - DAY   46

     The four kids walk toward the library.

                        XANDER
              So I'm Ted the sickly loser, I'm
              dying and my wife dumps me. I
              build a better Ted. He brings her
              back. she dies in his little love
              bunker and so he keeps bringing
              her back over and over. That's
              creepy on a level I hardly knew
              existed.

                        WILLOW
              And the sad thing is, the real Ted
              must have been a genius. There
              were design features in that robot
              that predate --

                        BUFFY
              Willow. Tell me you didn't keep
              any parts.

                        WILLOW
                    (guilty)
              Not any big ones...

                        BUFFY
              Oh, Will, you're supposed to use
              your powers for good!

                        WILLOW
              I just wanna learn stuff.

                                                        CONTINUED

46 CONTINUED: 46

                    CORDELIA
          Like how to build your own serial
          killer?

                    XANDER
          Well, it's hard to rent one
          nowadays.

                    CORDELIA
          Can't we just drop the subject?

                    BUFFY
          Absolutely. The whole incident is
          just something I plan to forget.
          I want to pick up right where we
          left off --

As she says it, she opens the door to the library, starts in--
and stops. She closes the door (we don't see what's in
there, though the kids all do) and turns to go, in high
dudgeon.

                    BUFFY (cont'd)
          That's it. I give up. Do I have
          to sound an air horn every time I
          enter a room?

She storms off, the others in tow. The camera tracks
forward, to see through the little window:

                    BUFFY (O.S.)
          I mean, what is it with grown ups
          these days?

Giles and Jenny, standing in the middle of the library.
Necking.

                                   BLACK OUT.

               END OF SHOW

BUFFY THE VAMPIRE SLAYER

"Bad Eggs"

Written By

Marti Noxon

Directed By

David Greenwalt

SHOOTING SCRIPT

November 10, 1997

BUFFY THE VAMPIRE SLAYER

"Bad Eggs"

CAST LIST

BUFFY SUMMERS......................... Sarah Michelle Gellar
XANDER HARRIS........................ Nicholas Brendon
RUPERT GILES......................... Anthony S. Head
WILLOW ROSENBERG..................... Alyson Hannigan
CORDELIA CHASE....................... Charisma Carpenter
ANGEL................................ David Boreanaz

JOYCE SUMMERS........................*Kristine Sutherland
HANDSOME COWBOY.(LYLE GORCH)..........*Jeremy Ratchford
TECTOR GORCH.........................*James Parks
GIRL.................................*Brie McCaddin
MR. WHITMORE.........................*Rick Zieff
JOHNATHAN............................*Danny Strong
*NIGHTWATCHMAN.......................*Eric Whitmore

BUFFY THE VAMPIRE SLAYER

"Bad Eggs"

SET LIST

INTERIORS

SUNNYDALE HIGH SCHOOL
    HALL
    LIBRARY
    MR. WHITMORE'S CLASSROOM
    SCIENCE CLASSROOM
    BROOM CLOSET/JANITOR'S CLOSET
    BOILER ROOM
BUFFY'S HOUSE
    BUFFY'S BEDROOM
    KITCHEN
WILLOW'S BEDROOM
SUNNYDALE MALL
    ANOTHER PART OF MALL/ESCALATOR
    HALLWAY OUTSIDE ARCADE
    ARCADE
    FOOD COURT
JOYCE'S CAR
TUNNEL
GROUNDSKEEPER'S SHED
UNDERGROUND CAVE

EXTERIORS

SUNNYDALE HIGH
    FRONT ENTRANCE
    GROUNDSKEEPER'S SHED
BUFFY'S HOUSE
CEMETERY

BUFFY THE VAMPIRE SLAYER

"Bad Eggs"

TEASER

1 INT.   SUNNYDALE MALL - NIGHT   1

BUFFY and JOYCE walk along. They have a couple of bags.
Buffy is in wheedle mode, but it's not working.

> BUFFY
> Come on, Mom, please?

> JOYCE
> I'm sorry, honey.

> BUFFY
> But... don't you understand? This is
> so important!

> JOYCE
> It's an outfit. An outfit that you
> may never buy.

> BUFFY
> But... I looked good in it!

> JOYCE
> You looked like a streetwalker!

> BUFFY
> But a **thin** streetwalker!
>   (beat)
> That's probably not gonna be the
> winning argument, is it?

> JOYCE
> You're just too young to wear that.

> BUFFY
> I'm gonna be too young to wear that
> till I'm too old to wear that.

> JOYCE
> That's the plan...
>   (looking at her watch)
> Oh, Stores are gonna close and I
> still need to order the flyers for
> the opening.

Joyce makes a decision. Looks through her purse and finds a
receipt.

                                                    CONTINUED

1 CONTINUED: 1

                         JOYCE (cont'd)
               Okay. I'll go to the printers and
               then get our food. You go pick up my
               outfit from the tailors at Everyday
               Woman. Here's the receipt--

                         BUFFY
               "Everyday Woman?" Why didn't you go
               straight to "Muumuus R Us"?

     Joyce points Buffy in the right direction.

                         JOYCE
               Do now. Make fun of your mother
               later.

     Buffy heads off on her mission. Joyce also moves off.

2 INT. ANOTHER PART OF MALL/ESCALATOR - CONTINUOUS - NIGHT 2

     Buffy walks toward "Everyday Woman", a totally "L7" clothing
     store. She can't help but notice a YOUNG, STUDLY GUY in
     western-style clothes, who's clearly hitting on a CUTE GIRL.
     The girl sits on a bench outside the store. He stands by
     her, one foot on the bench. He talks, she laughs shyly.

     Buffy turns to head into the store, then stops.

     ANGLE: MIRROR ALONG THE ESCALATOR

     shows the reflection of the girl. Alone. She gets up.

     Buffy turns, all business, as the (vampire) cowboy heads the
     girl toward a hallway. Buffy looks around, then slowly heads
     after them.

3 INT. HALLWAY OUTSIDE ARCADE - CONTINUOUS - NIGHT   3

     Buffy comes to an arcade, stops. The place is closed, but
     the security gate has been jimmied open. She listens, then
     starts forward.

4 INT. ARCADE   4

     Cowboy (LYLE GORCH) and girl are already up against a video
     game, kissing playfully. He has his hat off, his face buried
     in her neck.

                         LYLE
               You know... you got about the
               prettiest neck I've ever seen.

                                                          CONTINUED

4 CONTINUED: 4

                    BUFFY
          Wow, you guys really don't ever come
          up with new lines, do you?

He turns to face Buffy, standing some fifteen feet away. He
is in VAMP FACE, growling. The girl, not noticing the
change, turns to Buffy also.

                    GIRL
          Do you mind? We were talkin' here.

                    BUFFY
               (to the vamp)
          But you promised you'd never cheat on
          me again, honey...

                    GIRL
               (uncomfortable)
          Uh, I better go...

Lyle turns on her, growls.

                    LYLE
          I ain't done yet.

She starts back in horror, then takes off at a good clip.

Lyle steps up toward Buffy.

                    LYLE (cont'd)
          All right then, sugarlips. I'm all
          yours.

He lunges for her and she sends him reeling with a series of
blows. He falls back, coming back up in vamp face.

                    LYLE (cont'd)
          You're a rough one, ain't ya? I like
          that.

In a FLASH he comes at her. They trade blows but he gets in
close. He gets a hold of her, lifts her HIGH off the ground
and SLAMS her into the WALL.

                    LYLE (cont'd)
               (leering)
          A pretty little tidbit like you with
          so much kick... Have to be the
          slayer I've been hearing so much
          about- Lyle Gorch. Pleased to meet
          you.

                                            CONTINUED

4 CONTINUED: (2)   4

In answer, Buffy viciously KNEES him in the FACE. He drops
her and she SWEEP KICKS his legs out from under him.

                    BUFFY
          Pleasure's mine.

She STRADDLES him, producing a STAKE from her jacket.

She RAISES the STAKE. But Lyle manages to ROLL OUT FROM
UNDER HER and get to his feet. They are both breathing hard,
and the humor is gone from his gaze.

                    LYLE
          This ain't over, girl.

And he's gone. Buffy, winded, does not give chase.

                    BUFFY
          Oh, sure... they **say** they'll call...

5 INT. FOOD COURT - NIGHT   5

Buffy's mom is now sitting at the table with dinner. Buffy
comes to the table, looking a little worse for the wear. She
sits.

                    BUFFY
          Oh, bliss. Mall food.

She starts to eat. Joyce just looks at her.

                    JOYCE
          Buffy.

                    BUFFY
          Mom.

                    JOYCE
          Where's my dress.

                    BUFFY
          Your--?
                    (realizing)
          Oh. Oh my God.

                    JOYCE
          Buffy, what were you -- no, let me
          guess. You were distracted by a boy.

                    BUFFY
          Technically.

                                                        CONTINUED

5 CONTINUED: 5

                          JOYCE
              Buffy...

                          BUFFY
              Well, I'll get it --

                          JOYCE
              They're closed. I'll have to fit it
              in tomorrow.

Buffy sits, contrite.

                          BUFFY
              Sorry.

                          JOYCE
              A little responsibility, Buffy,
              that's all I ask. Honestly, don't
              you ever think about anything besides
              boys and clothes?

                          BUFFY
              Saving the world from vampires.

Joyce stares at her.

                          JOYCE
              I swear, sometimes I have no idea
              what does on in your head.

Off Buffy's look...

                                        BLACK OUT

                      END OF TEASER

ACT ONE

6 INT. BROOM CLOSET - DAY   6

BLACK

Out of the darkness we hear the sound of SMOOTCHIES.

                    XANDER (O.C.)
          Ummmmmm.

                    CORDELIA (O.C.)
          Ohhhhhh.

Then two familiar voices-

                    CORDELIA (cont'd; O.C.)
          Xander?

                    XANDER (O.C.)
          Shhhhh.

                    CORDELIA
          I'm just worried that we're going to
          miss class-

A beat. An overhead light comes on.

In the light, XANDER and CORDELIA back away from each other.

                    XANDER
          You know. It's really better for me
          if you don't talk.

                    CORDELIA
          Well. It's really better for me with
          the lights off.

She reaches for the STRING that turns the light off.

BLACK

Sound of SMOOTCHIES AGAIN. For a beat.

Then another CLICK-

The lights are BACK ON. Now Xander holds the string.

                    XANDER
          Are you saying you can't look at me
          when we... whatever we do?

                                          CONTINUED

6 CONTINUED: 6

                         CORDELIA
               It's not that I can't. It's more
               that I... don't want to.

                         XANDER
               That's great. That's just dandy.
               We're repulsed by each other. We
               hide from our friends--

                         CORDELIA
                    (horrified)
               I should hope. Please.

                         XANDER
               All and all. This thing is not what
               I'd call a self-esteem booster.

                         CORDELIA
               Tell me about it. I mean, look at
               you. Where did you get those shoes?

                         XANDER
               Okay. You know what? I don't need
               this.

He reaches for the door. Cordelia follows suit.

                         CORDELIA
               Ditto. Like a hole in the head.

Their hands touch. That's all it takes. They're all over
each other - wild with... inexplicable... passion.

As they LOWER OUT OF FRAME, Cordelia grabs the string to the
light.

BLACK

                                        PRELAP:

                    MR. WHITMORE (V.O.)
               Sex!!

FADE UP ON:

7 INT. MR. WHITMORE'S CLASSROOM - DAY   7

WILLOW, Xander and Cordelia (both looking a bit mussed) are
in TEEN HEALTH CLASS, which is taught by a slight, somewhat
nebbishy guy, MR. WHITMORE.

                                             CONTINUED

7 CONTINUED:

There are posters on the wall about vegetables, teen
pregnancy, that sort of stuff. Mr. Whitmore is pacing while
the assembled class looks on.

                    MR. WHITMORE
          The sex drive in the human animal is
          intense--

Willow squirms uncomfortably as DAVE, an ENORMOUS, DUMB JOCK
looks over at her, smiles.

                    MR. WHITMORE (cont'd)
          How many of us have lost countless
          productive hours plagued by unwanted
          sexual thoughts and feelings -- ?

Xander's hand shoots up.

                    MR. WHITMORE (cont'd)
          That was a rhetorical question, Mr.
          Harris. Not a poll.

                    XANDER
          Oh.

Hand goes down.

                    MR. WHITMORE
          Of course, for teenagers such as
          yourselves these feelings are even
          more overwhelming. With all sorts of
          hormones surging through your bodies,
          compelling you to action - it's often
          difficult to remember that there are
          negative consequences to having sex.
          Would anyone care to offer one such
          consequence?

Cordelia's hand shoots up.

                    CORDELIA
          That depends. Are you talking about
          sex in a car or out of a car?
          Because one time - a friend of mine,
          not me - kicked the gear shift in a
          Miata that was parked at the top of
          this hill and--

                    MR. WHITMORE
               (interrupting her)
          I was thinking of something a little
          more... commonplace, Ms. Chase.

                                             CONTINUED

7 CONTINUED: (2)   7

Xander, jealous despite himself, shoots Cordelia a look and
puts his hand up--

                    XANDER
          You want to talk negative
          consequence? How about the
          heartbreak of halitosis? I mean, a
          girl may seem spiffy, but if she
          ignores her flossing, the bloom is
          definitely off the rose--

And now Cordelia's hand is up again.

                    CORDELIA
          Like that compares to kissing a guy   *
          who thinks the Hoover technique is a   *
          big turn on--   *

                    MR. WHITMORE
          Okay. Anyone--

                    XANDER
          What about having to feign interest   *
          in her vapid little chit-chat just to   *
          get some touch? Book cut jeans, pro   *
          or con? Can you say - get a life!?   *

                                                                 *

ON CLASS

Who are all intently watching them. Xander and Cordy
suddenly realize they are in the spotlight. Oops.

                    MR. WHITMORE
          Now? Another consequence of sexual
          activity? Anyone?

Cordelia is about to speak --

                    MR. WHITMORE (cont'd)
          -- else?

                    WILLOW
          How about pregnancy? That would be
          a major one - right?

                    MR. WHITMORE
          Thank you, Ms. Rosenberg. Among
          teens, unwanted pregnancy would be
          the number one negative consequence
          of sexual activity.
                    (more)

                                                       CONTINUED

7 CONTINUED: (3)   7

                    MR. WHITMORE (cont'd)
          This is partly because some teens
          think of a baby as a toy, or as a
          companion who will give them love.
          The truth, of course, is that a child
          is a relentless, needy tyrant. So,
          as discussed last week, I've devised
          an exercise that may give you some
          idea of what an enormous burden
          having your own tiny charge can be--

Whitmore moves to his desk - uncovers a FULL CRATE OF EGGS he
has hidden there.

                    MR. WHITMORE (cont'd)
          Ladies and gentlemen. I present you
          with your offspring. Your assignment
          is as follows. You will split into
          parenting teams. You and your
          partner will share equally in the
          daily task of "raising" your egg.

He holds up a small composition notebook.

                    MR. WHITMORE (cont'd)
          Every aspect of your child's care
          will be recorded in this daily log.
          If your egg breaks - you have killed
          your child. Naturally, this will
          affect your grade. Now, please
          choose a partner and pick up your
          children.

There is general hubbub in the room as people scramble to
pair up.

ON XANDER AND CORDELIA

Who glare at each other. Then Cordelia turns and grabs a
BUFF BABE.

Xander follows suit, sidling up to a CUTE LITTLE MUFFIN, who
has already been assigned an egg.

                    XANDER
                 (to Muffin)
          I know we just met, but isn't that
          Xander Jr. you're holding?

The girl giggles. Cordelia sees this, turns away - annoyed.

                                                      CONTINUED

7   CONTINUED: (4)   7

ON WILLOW

Who sees DAVE barrelling toward her. She looks desperately
around for another partner. But everyone is already attached.

Off Willow's despair--

8   INT. LIBRARY - DAY   8

Willow and Xander enter. Willow carries a small EGG CARTON
with her.

Buffy is there, looking through some books.

                    WILLOW
          Buffy. How come you weren't in class?

                    BUFFY
          Vampire issues. Did Mister Whitmore
          notice that I was tardy?

                    XANDER
          I think the word you're searching for
          is 'absent'.

                    WILLOW
                (agreeing)
          Tardy people show.

                    BUFFY
          Oh. Right.

                    WILLOW
          And, yes, he noticed. So he wanted
          me to give you this.

Willow hands BUFFY an EGG. Buffy takes it, puzzled.

                    BUFFY
          As punishments go, this is fairly
          abstract.

                    WILLOW
          No, it's your baby.

                    BUFFY
          Okay, I get it even less.

                                          CONTINUED

8 CONTINUED: 8

                                  XANDER
You know, it's the whole "sex leads
to responsibility" thing, which I
really don't get. You gotta take
care of the egg, it's a baby, gotta
keep it safe and teach it Christian
values.

                                  WILLOW
My egg is jewish.

                                  XANDER
Then teach it that dreidel song.

                                  BUFFY
God, I can't do this... I can't take
care of stuff! I killed my gigapet.
Literally! I sat on it and it broke.

She puts her egg on the counter.

                                  WILLOW
You'll do fine.

                                  XANDER
The only thing that stresses me is,
when do we tell them they're adopted?

                                  BUFFY
I'll just lay it all off on my
partner. Who'd I get?

                                  WILLOW
Well. There was an uneven number of
kids - and you didn't show, so...

                                  BUFFY
I'm a single mother?

                                  XANDER
No man of her own...

                                  WILLOW
At least you're not paired with
Gordon the pig boy.

                                  BUFFY
What does this say about me? That
I'm doomed to live my mother's life?
How deeply scary is that?

CONTINUED

8 CONTINUED: (2)   8

                    XANDER
          How about this - it says nothing. It
          means nothing. This whole egg
          experiment is completely pointless--

GILES emerges from the stacks - dusty volume in hand, natch.

                    GILES
          Success at last. Your new playmate
          is a fellow of some repute, it seems.

He puts the book down -- almost on Buffy's egg. She snatches
it to safety at the last second, looks at the book.

CLOSE ON

An old photograph of LYLE, the cowboy vamp, and another guy
in western garb. The other fellow is a big, lumbering sort.

                    GILES (O.C.)
          Lyle Gorch. The other one is his
          brother Tector. They're from
          Abeline. Made their reputation
          massacring a mexican village in 1886.

                    BUFFY
          Friendly little demons...

                    GILES
          No, that was before they became
          vampires.
               (off their looks)   *
          The good news is, they're not among   *
          the great thinkers of our time. I
          doubt they're up to much; They were
          probably just drawn here by the
          hellmouth's energy.

                    XANDER
          Enough said. I propose that Buffy
          slays them. All in favor?

                    WILLOW
               (raises her hand)
          Aye.

                                                    CONTINUED

8 CONTINUED: (3)   8

                    BUFFY
          Great. Now I have to worry about
          Butch and Sundance while I'm taking
          care of junior here.

                    GILES
          You might need some help with those
          two, they are pretty --
               (stops, puzzled)
          Why do you all have eggs?

                    WILLOW
               (delighted)
          Hey. Maybe Angel could help you find
          the Gorches.

                    GILES
          Good idea. You really ought to
          strengthen your numbers when you go
          up against these two.

                    XANDER
          Oh right. I see a lot of "hunting"
          getting done in that scenario. Angel
          and Buffy. Alone. Late at night.

                    Buffy
               (to Xander)
          Please. Like Angel and I are just
          helpless slaves to passion. Grow up.

9 EXT.   CEMETERY - NIGHT   9

     Buffy and ANGEL are leaning against a tree. Kissing madly.
     It's pretty hot. Finally, Buffy breaks away.

                    BUFFY
          We should--

                    ANGEL
          I know--

     They start to kiss again. Then--

                    BUFFY
          Yeah, this really isn't "hunting" in
          the classical sense. We should get
          to work.

                    ANGEL
          You're right. Okay.

                                                        CONTINUED

9 CONTINUED: 9

Angel tries to pull it together, as does Buffy. They move
away from the tree, walk a bit.

                    BUFFY
          You see anything?

                    ANGEL
          No.

                    BUFFY
          Okay. Enough hunting.

She jumps him. They fall together again, laughing.

ON GORCH BROTHERS

Who are hidden behind a large tomb. Watching Buffy and Angel
neck.

As in the picture, Lyle's older brother, TECTOR, is a large,
graceless guy. He's not the sharpest tool in the shed - but
what he lacks in brains he makes up for in sheet, brutish
power. Like Lyle, he speaks with a Texas srawl.

                    TECTOR
          That's the Slayer?

                    LYLE
          Yep.

                    TECTOR
          And ain't that Angelus with her?

                    LYLE
          Yep.

                    TECTOR
          Well, then, how come she's not
          slaying and how come he's--

                    LYLE
          I don't know, Tector. How come you
          always have to ask so many damn
          questions?

                    TECTOR
              (impressed)
          So that's Angelus. The Angelus.
              (then)
          You gonna take him, or you want me
          to, Lyle?

                                                    CONTINUED

9 CONTINUED: (2)   9

                        LYLE
          I say we leave it. Get her when
          she's alone.

                        TECTOR
          Why? You scared?

                        LYLE
          'Course not. I could whip both of
          em' right now.

                        TECTOR
          So why don't you?

                        LYLE
                (flaring)
          Listen. I got a plan. You leave the
          thinking to me, remember? Don't I
          always take care of you?

Lyle starts to move off and Tector follows. As they
disappear into the darkness--

                        TECTOR (O.C.)
          I know, Lyle. You do the thinking.
          That's your department.
                (then)
          So tell me again why we can't kill em
          now?

                                        FADE TO:

10 INT.   BUFFY'S BEDROOM - NIGHT   10

Buffy, dressed for sleep, enters with her egg in a makeshift
"bed" - a little basket that is lined with dish towels. She
sets him down on her windowsill - arranges his covers.

                        BUFFY
          Alrighty then egg dud--

She checks her "egg log" - a written diary (in the small
composition notebook) of the egg's daily schedule.

                        BUFFY (cont'd)
          Feeding. Check. Burping. Check.
          Diapers. Check.
                (adjusts the towel
                 around the egg)
          Sort of. In theory.
                (to egg)
          Okay, kid. Sweet dreams.

                                                    CONTINUED

10   CONTINUED: 10

     She gives him a nice pat. Goes to her bed and climbs in.
     Lights out.

                                        DISSOLVE TO:

11   EXT. BUFFY'S HOUSE - NIGHT   11

     We move toward the house. Ominously. Something wicked this
     way comes.

12   INT. BUFFY'S BEDROOM - LATER - NIGHT   12

     Buffy is now sound asleep. We move across her still form to
     the WINDOW. Is there movement there, or is it just a shadow?

     Then, suddenly, a chip of shell spontaneously BREAKS from
     Buffy's egg. And a single, hairy TENDRIL emerges from the
     crack.

     The tendril silently snakes across the windowsill, clearly
     heading for BUFFY.

                                        BLACK OUT.

                    END OF ACT ONE

ACT TWO

13   INT. BUFFY'S BEDROOM - NIGHT   13

Back to the tendril. Now it's made it's way over to Buffy's
bed. It slides up the covers, over her legs and chest,
winding it's way up to her FACE.

When it arrives, the tendril FLATTENS AND WIDENS, covering
her face like a black mask. Then it starts to PULSE, gently,
persistently.

Moving from the tendril to the egg - we see that the egg
itself has started to GLOW, ever so faintly.

                                              CUT TO:

14   INT. TUNNEL - EARLY MORNING   14

CLOSE ON: A DEAD RAT

as it is thrown to the floor.

                         TECTOR
                    I'm tired of rat. I want something
                    good to eat.

They are huddled against the wall. Early morning rays shine
through a grate at the other end of the tunnel.

                         LYLE
                    We'll get you the good stuff. Just
                    gotta be patient.

                         TECTOR
                    Why can't we stay in a nice place?
                    A motel or something, with an ice
                    machine.

                         LYLE
                    Gotta keep a low profile till we've
                    taken care of this Slayer.

                         TECTOR
                    How come Angelus is gettin' all
                    snuggly with her? Does the man have
                    no code?

                         LYLE
                    Are you gonna pester me with
                    questions all the damn day?

                                                       CONTINUED

14 CONTINUED: 14

                    TECTOR
          I just don't like it here. I'm cold,
          and I'm bored and there ain't a
          decent whore in the whole city limits.

                    LYLE
          Well, this is the thanks I get.
          Don't I always look after you?
          Didn't I near raise you myself?
          Burden that you were, I shoulda left
          you on a doorstep when mama blew town.

                    TECTOR
          Oh, don't say that...

                    LYLE
          Now, I'm taking care of this. We'll
          hit the Slayer when she's down, when
          she ain't looking. Then this town is
          ours.

                    TECTOR
          Are you afraid of her?

                    LYLE
          Playing it safe, is all. We'll
          follow her some more. Find out time.
          This ain't over.

                    TECTOR
               (schoolyard taunt)
          You're afraid of the Slayer...

                    LYLE
          You want me to sit your ass down in
          that sunlight?

                    TECTOR
          Think you can?

                    LYLE
          Come on!

They start rasslin', just like brothers.

                    TECTOR
          Is that all you got? Is that all you
          got....?

15   INT. BUFFY'S BEDROOM - LATER - DAY   15

The sun now bathes the room in light, washing away all signs
of ultra creepy weirdness.

The egg looks COMPLETELY NORMAL again, except for the fact
that it seems too big for its bowl today.

Buffy's ALARM goes off and she wakes painfully, barely able
to raise a weak arm to turn the thing off. She sits on the
edge of her bed, feeling horrible.

                    BUFFY
          Oh, God...

She gets up and goes to the egg. Sees that it appears to be
larger today, but shrugs it off. Picks it up in its little
basket.

26   INT. BUFFY'S KITCHEN - DAY   16

Buffy comes into the kitchen, dragging. She's dressed for
school and carries her egg in its little basket. Her mother
is pouring herself coffee -- Buffy takes the cup and sips it,
makes a face.

                    JOYCE
          At least eat something if you're
          going to drink that.

                    BUFFY
          Not that hungry.

                    JOYCE
          How goes the parenting?

                    BUFFY
          Fine.

                    JOYCE
          You sure your egg is secure in there?

                    BUFFY
          Did I ask for backseat mommying?

                    JOYCE
          Sorry. Are we a little touchy this
          morning?

                    BUFFY
          I just feel all funky.

Joyce feels her forehead.

                                                    CONTINUED

16 CONTINUED: 16

                    JOYCE
          You don't have a temperature.

                    BUFFY
          It's not that - I just didn't sleep
          well.

                    JOYCE
          What's the matter - did your egg keep
          you up all night?

                    BUFFY
          You're killing me.   *

She picks up a muffin and her egg case as she heads out.

                    BUFFY (cont'd)
          Parenting is a pain.

                    JOYCE
          Wait till it starts dating.

ANGLE: THE COUNTER

Where the egg case was, there is a bit of blue goo.

17 INT. LIBRARY - DAY   17

Giles is re-shelving some books when Buffy, Xander and Willow
enter.

                    GILES
          Why are you three about? Don't you
          have class?

                    WILLOW
          Teen health got canceled.

                    XANDER
          Mr. Whitmore's out today - couldn't
          get an egg-sitter or something.

Both Willow and Buffy are obviously out of it. They sit
heavily. Buffy lays her head on the table.

                    GILES
          Well, then could you give me a hand?

                    BUFFY/WILLOW
          No.

Xander, however, goes up the steps to Giles, starts helping.

                                                       CONTINUED

17 CONTINUED: 17

                          GILES
             How did the hunt go last night, Buffy?

                          BUFFY
             No go.

                          GILES
             You didn't go, or you were
             unsuccessful?

                          BUFFY
             No Gorches.

                          XANDER
             Apparently, Buffy has decided that
             the problem with the English language
             is all those pesky words.
                   (to Buffy)
             You. Angel. Big. Smoochies?

                          BUFFY
             Shut. Up.

                          GILES
             It's true. You and Willow do appear
             to be awfully sluggish. Are you
             quite sure you're alright?

                          WILLOW
             Maybe it was something we ate...

                          XANDER
             Or perhaps it's the burden of
             parenthood. Notice how seriously
             both of you have taken this egg
             thing - while I, in turn, chose a
             more balanced approach--

He produces his egg from a jacket pocket. Starts tossing it
in the air and catching it as he talks. Willow is watching
his egg - nervous.

                          WILLOW
             Xander. Maybe you shouldn't--

                          XANDER
             See? That's just what I'm talking
             about. You can't stress over every
             little thing. A child picks up on
             that - which is a one-way ticket to
             neurotic city--

                                                              CONTINUED

17 CONTINUED: (2)   17

This time he misses the catch. Willow, Buffy and Giles GASP.

CLOSE ON EGG

SLO MO - as it falls to the carpet. But instead of
breaking - it BOUNCES. Rolls to a stop.

BACK ON GANG

                    WILLOW
          It didn't break!
                    (then)
          Why didn't it break?

Xander scoops the egg up.

                    XANDER
          That's the other secret to
          conscientious egg-care. A pot of
          scalding water and about eight
          minutes.

                    WILLOW
          You BOILED your young?

                    XANDER
          I know it sounds harsh. But
          sometimes you have to be harsh to be
          kind. You can bet little Xander here
          is thick-skinned now--

CLOSE ON SHELF AS GILES IS PUTTING A BOOK AWAY

We see AN EGG hidden among the books. Giles doesn't notice
it.

                    GILES
          Technically, that would be called
          cheating, yes?

                    XANDER
          No! It's just like taking a
          shortcut, you know, if you're running
          a race.

                    BUFFY
          That would also be cheating.

                    WILLOW
          You should be ashamed.

                                            CONTINUED

> GILES
> I suppose there is a sort of
> machiavellian ingenuity to your
> transgression...

> XANDER
> I resent that!... Or, possibly,
> thank you...

> GILES
> Bit of both would suit.

Cordelia enters, walks up to the table.

> CORDELIA
> Figures, you three are all hanging in
> the dungeon while something major is
> going on at Sunnydale High.

> XANDER
> And what would that be, Cordelia?
> Barrette appreciation day?

> CORDELIA
> Mr. Whitmore didn't show today.

> BUFFY
> That news is of the past.

> CORDELIA
> He can't be reached. He's **missing**.
> And presumed dead.

> GILES
> Presumed by whom?

> CORDELIA
> Well, me.

> GILES
> I think we might wait a few hours
> before we give up on him completely.

> CORDELIA
> Well I think we should look around.
> Don't you, Xander?

She gives him a pointed look, revealing her ulterior
motive -- but not to him.

> XANDER
> It can wait.

17 CONTINUED: (4)   17

                    BUFFY
          You're awfully gung-ho.

                    CORDELIA
               (to Xander)
          Well, his body could fall out of a
          closet somewhere. We should check
          every closet to see if he's in a
          closet.

Xander gets it.

                    XANDER
          Of course. There could be a
          closet... Let's go.

He heads down, the two of them heading out as he instructs
the others:

                    XANDER (cont'd)
          You guys look for other clues. We'll
          meet back here.

                    BUFFY
               (no intention of
                stirring)
          We'll get right on that.

                    WILLOW
               (watches them leave)
          Are they getting weirder? Have you
          noticed the weirdness of them?

                    BUFFY
          I don't know. Should we be having
          guilt about not looking for Mr.
          Whitmore?

                    GILES
          I think you can hold off on that.
          I'd prefer you save your strength for
          hunting the Gorches.

                    BUFFY
          Yeah, I'll be fine by tonight. Maybe
          sweep the cemetery.

                    GILES
          Be careful. If you're still feeling
          sluggish --

                    BUFFY
          No worries.

                                              CONTINUED

17 CONTINUED: (5)   17

                              WILLOW
                    And you've got Angel helping you,
                    right?

                              BUFFY
                    Yeah, he, uh... does what he can.

18 EXT. GRAVEYARD - NIGHT   18

        Angel and Buffy are leaning against a tomb this time. Major
        league necking. Finally, they come up for air.

                              BUFFY
                    As much as I hate to say this - we
                    should go kill bad guys.

                              ANGEL
                    It's late. You should go home.

                              BUFFY
                    What about the Gorches?

                              ANGEL
                    I'll hunt.

                              BUFFY
                    Really? You'd do that?

                              ANGEL
                    It's not like I have an early day
                    tomorrow.

                              BUFFY
                    True. And I still have to go home
                    and fill out my egg diary.

                              ANGEL
                    Your - what?

                              BUFFY
                    I told you. That faux parenting gig
                    I'm doing in school.
                         (then)
                    Like I'm really planning to have kids
                    any time soon. Someday, when I'm
                    done having a life maybe. A kid
                    would be too much to deal with now.

                                                              CONTINUED

18 CONTINUED: 18

                    ANGEL
          I wouldn't know.
                    (then/carefully)
          I don't... Well, you know, I can't.

This sinks in.

                    BUFFY
          Oh.
                    (then/re-grouping)
          Well, it's totally okay. I figured   *
          there are all kinds of things
          vampires can't do like, you know,
          work for the telephone company,
          volunteer for the red cross. Have
          little vampires...

                    ANGEL
                    (skeptical)
          So you don't think about the future.

                    BUFFY
          No.

                    ANGEL
          Never.

                    BUFFY
          No.

                    ANGEL
          How can you say that? You're not
          like me. You could have a normal
          life.
                    (off her look)
          You know what I mean. Less not   *
          normal. You really don't care what
          happens a year from now? Five years
          from now -- ?

                    BUFFY
          I - I can't care.
                    (with difficulty)
          Angel. When I try to look into the
          future, all I can see... is you--

Angel shakes his head.

                    ANGEL
                    (pained)
          Buffy--

                                                        CONTINUED

18 CONTINUED: (2)   18

                         BUFFY
              And I don't have a choice. Don't you
              know that? If I could do the logic
              thing, you think I would even be here?
                    (then)
              All I can see is you... All I want
              is you.

     A beat. Finally - Angel nods. Giving into it.

                         ANGEL
                    (quietly)
              I know the feeling.

     He draws her back into his arms. They kiss tenderly,
     passionately. Tomorrow entirely forgotten.

19 INT. HALLWAY AT SCHOOL - NIGHT   19

     The NIGHTWATCHMAN walks down the hall, checking door. He
     finds the door to the BOILER ROOM ajar. Goes in.

20 INT. BOILER ROOM - NIGHT   20

     He comes in, tries the light. It doesn't work. He goes
     slowly down the steps, shining his flash light around.

     There is a noise from the back of the room. He heads that
     way, still slow and careful. He reaches the corner and finds:

     ANGLE: A HOLE

     Dug in the wall. A pool of darkness that the guard moves
     slowly toward, brows furrowed. He moves closer. Sticks his
     head in.

     Mr. Whitmore steps up behind him and gives him a violent
     SHOVE into the hole. We hear the guard tumble, screaming,
     then hit the ground hard.

     Whitmore is dirty, sweaty -- and completely expressionless.
     Picking up a pick axe, he steps into the hole.

21 INT. BUFFY'S BEDROOM - NIGHT   21

     We see the egg in f.g. on Buffy's night table next to her
     bed. It moves slightly, accompanied by a tiny CLICKING
     sound, then stops. RACK TO F.G. as Buffy climbs in her
     window.

                                                          CONTINUED

21 CONTINUED: 21

Buffy moves towards us, perhaps a little dreamy still from
her "hunt" with Angel.

CLOSER - Buffy, hearing the CLICKING sound. She looks around,
then she looks down.

The egg is large in frame, moving slightly as Buffy leans in,
curious, her face getting closer and closer to the egg.

ANGLE - THE EGG

Still. Then jiggling a little. Then still.

BUFFY - moves even closer

THE EGG (Buffy is not in this shot) - explodes! (Special
effects.)

BUFFY - leaps back, horrified.

C.G.I. SHOT -- a horrible and slimy creature bursts out of
the shells. And leaps at camera.

BUFFY DUCKS -- the creature just misses her -- Buffy spins in
time to see:

ANGLE THE FLOOR -- (Puppeteer shot) The creature skitters
across the floor going in front of the bed. From Buffy's POV
it could very well have gone underneath it.

BUFFY - Never taking her eyes off the bed, she backs to a
shelf, picks up a large book to squash the creature with.
Creeps back towards the bed, kneels down. Carefully picks up
the dust ruffle.

REVERSE ANGLE - The dust ruffle is pulled back, revealing
Buffy's face. She looks past camera carefully, creepily.
Nothing.

BUFFY - slowly gets up, looks around. She turns slowly
around. No creature... she keeps turning, eying every corner
of the room. still no creature... until it falls on her from
above. Hitting her neck, trying to scuttle down the back of
her blouse.

Buffy drops the book, grabs the creature with both hands,
struggling with it, flings it off her.

ANGLE - FLOOR NEAR VANITY - (Puppeteer shot) - The creature
skitters under the vanity.

Buffy hears more skittering.

                                                    CONTINUED

21 CONTINUED: (2)   21

     Buffy's POV - moving from the vanity towards the bookshelves.

     Buffy hurls open a vanity drawer, grabs a SHARP LETTER
     OPENER, stalks towards the shelves. HEARS MORE SKITTERING.

     POV - WHIP PAN from the shelves to behind Buffy's bedside
     table where the cracked egg shells reside. Buffy moves
     closer and closer to the end table, letter opener ready to
     stab.

     ANGEL - BUFFY - Moving towards camera. Behind her on the
     wall, slightly out of focus (puppeteer shot) we see the
     creature moving up the wall.

     Buffy looks down at the end table as the creature moves just
     a little higher on the wall right behind her. The sound so
     soft only a Slayer might hear it. She cocks her head
     slightly, still looking towards us and -- without turning --
     whips her hand back and nails the sucker right in the middle
     of it's horrid body. Then she pulls letter opener and
     creature out of wall and slams it on the ground, stabbing it
     again. Blue goo dribbles out of the creature and it lies
     still.

                         BUFFY
               Yuck.

     Buffy, shook, stares down at the creature, then leans over
     and grabs the the chord to her phone, pulling phone off night
     stand and onto the floor. She dials hurriedly.

                         BUFFY (cont'd)
               Come on, pick up.

     INTERCUT WITH

22 INT. WILLOW'S BEDROOM - NIGHT   22

     Willow, awake, answers her phone.

                         WILLOW
               Hello?

                         BUFFY
               Willow. Are you okay?

                         WILLOW
               Why shouldn't I be?

                                                      CONTINUED

22 CONTINUED: 22

                    BUFFY
          Your egg. Is it doing anything?   *

                    WILLOW   *
          Doing what?   *

                    BUFFY   *
          Break it. Right now. Smash it with   *
          something heavy.   *

                    WILLOW   *
          Buffy, what--   *

                    BUFFY   *
          My egg just went postal on me. It   *
          hatched - some kind of crawly monster   *
          thing jumped on me--   *

                    WILLOW   *
          Are you okay?   *

                    BUFFY   *
          Yeah, but your egg--   *

                    WILLOW   *
          It's totally normal. I put it in the   *
          fridge.   *

                    BUFFY   *
          Okay...   *

                    WILLOW
          Maybe it was a trap. Something the
          Gorch brothers planted for you.

                    BUFFY
          Maybe...
               (pulls it together)
          Okay. I'm sorry to wake you. Get
          back to sleep.

                    WILLOW
          You sure?

                    BUFFY
          Yeah. I'm better. I'm fine.

     ON WILLOW

                    WILLOW
          Okay. I'll see you tomorrow.

                                              CONTINUED

22 CONTINUED: (2)   22

Willow hangs up and we WIDEN to see her sitting at her desk,
looking straight ahead. Strangely emotionless.

Her EGG is right next to her. CONSPICUOUSLY HATCHED.

                                        BLACK OUT.

                    END OF ACT TWO

ACT THREE

23 INT. BUFFY'S BEDROOM - NIGHT   23

CLOSE ON CLOCK

It's 2:42 AM.

ON BUFFY

Who is hanging-up from her call with Willow.

                    JOYCE
               (entering)
          Buffy, who are you talking to at
          this...

Buffy hurriedly drapes a shirt over the creature as her
mother stops, staring at her.

                    JOYCE (cont'd)
          Why are you dressed? Where exactly
          do you think you're going at three
          o'clock in the morning?

                    BUFFY
          Nowhere --

                    JOYCE
          Who was that on the phone?

                    BUFFY
          It was Willow... I just called 'cause
          she wasn't feeling well and I was
          worried.

                    JOYCE
          You're gonna have to do better than
          that, young lady.

                    BUFFY
          I... had a bad dream...

                    JOYCE
          No, you're about to have a bad dream.
          A dream that you're grounded for the
          rest of your natural life --

Joyce's tirade carries into:

24   INT.   JOYCE'S CAR - DAY   24

     Buffy looks fried. She's in total lecture overload.

                         JOYCE
               ...Which means no after-school
               socializing. No Bronze. No nothing,
               not until I give you the say so. Do
               you understand?

                         BUFFY
               Yes. But--

                         JOYCE
               Yes or no. That's all I want to hear
               from you.

     Joyce pulls up in front of school.

                         JOYCE (cont'd)
               Now. School ends at 2:30. I want
               you to go to the library at 2:33 and
               study until I pick you up there at
               5:30. Understood?

                         BUFFY
               Yes.

                         JOYCE
               Good. Have a nice day.

     Buffy climbs out of the car. Mom takes off.

25   EXT.   SUNNYDALE HIGH - FRONT ENTRANCE - DAY   25

     All the kids are arriving for the day.

     Buffy sees CORDELIA and moves to her. Cordy, going with the
     a "sweet but naughty" schoolgirl look, carries an ADORABLE
     TEDDY BEAR BACKPACK.

                         BUFFY
               Nice bear. Listen, is your --

                         CORDELIA
               I'll have you know my father brought
               this back for me from Gstaad years
               ago. Then all of the sudden these
               trendoids everywhere are sporting
               them. So I've been totally not
               wearing it. But then I was - "Hey!
               I started this whole nation-wide
               craze. What am I ashamed of?"

                                                        CONTINUED

25 CONTINUED: 25

                    BUFFY
          Okay, soliloquy girl... I just
          wanted to know about your egg.

                    CORDELIA
          My egg?

                    BUFFY
          You know the egg that Mr. Whitmore
          gave to you?

                    CORDELIA
          I've got in my bear. I'm going to
          ace this experiment. No sweat. You
          think keeping an egg intact for a
          week is effortful? Try not breaking
          a silk-wrapped nail.

                    BUFFY
          And your egg isn't acting... odd or
          anything?

Cordy looks at her like this is the dumbest thing she's ever
heard.

                    CORDELIA
          It's not "acting" anything. It's an
          egg, Buffy. It doesn't emote.

She scoffs. They continue walking toward school.

ON XANDER

Who sits on one of the benches at the top of the stairs. He
pulls a cheesy-looking BREAKFAST BAR from his school bag and
unwraps it. It looks dry, unappetizing. He takes a bite.

                    XANDER
          Ummmm. Card-boardy.

He tosses it. Considers something. Then he reaches into his
pack - pulls out his egg.

                    XANDER (cont'd)
                  (to egg)
          Sorry, Junior. A man's gotta eat.

He cracks the egg on the bench. Rolls it.

ON WILLOW

Who joins Buffy and Cordy. Cordy is yakking with one of the
Cordettes - not paying Willow and Buffy any mind.

                                                    CONTINUED

25 CONTINUED: (2)   25

                         BUFFY
            Sorry about calling you so late last
            night.

                         WILLOW
            That's okay. I was awake.

                         BUFFY
            What were you doing up?

                         WILLOW
            Just couldn't sleep, I guess.
                 (then)
            So, was there any more "hatchling"
            activity last night?

                         BUFFY
            No. I think you may be right. My
            egg may have been some kind of booby
            trap the vamps laid for me. So far,
            it seems like everybody else's are
            normal.

                         WILLOW
            You didn't bring the "thing" that
            attacked you, did you?

                         BUFFY
            Yeah. I called Giles and he's in
            research mode. Wants to see it.

They move toward the front steps of the school.

                         WILLOW
            Well, take it to the science lab.
            I'll get Giles and we can analyze it.

                         BUFFY
            Great. I always say - a day without
            an autopsy is like a day without
            sunshine...

As they walk off we MOVE CLOSE to Willow's BACK - and see an
odd lump under her clothes. Two tentacles extend from under
her shirt and FUSE into her body at the base of her spinal
cord.

ON XANDER

who is about to bite into his hard-boiled egg.

                                                          CONTINUED

25   CONTINUED: (3)   25

CLOSE ON EGG

It's a HORRIBLE, DEFORMED hard-boiled MONSTER.   One bloodshot
EYE stares up at him.

BACK ON XANDER

As he takes in this gruesome sight.

ON BUFFY, WILLOW AND CORDELIA

Who all react to XANDER'S (O.C.) SCREAM.

26   INT. SCIENCE ROOM - DAY   26

CLOSE ON

The "thing" that hatched in Buffy's room and the egg that
Xander almost bit into. Both are laid out in dissection
trays.

ON BUFFY, XANDER, & CORDELIA

Who stare down at the things with varying levels of disgust.

                    XANDER
          Can I just say--
                    (he shudders)
          Uhhhhhhhhhhhhh.

                    BUFFY
          I see your uhhhhhhhhhhh and raise you
          a gnyeh.

                    CORDELIA
          What is it?

                    XANDER
          We don't know what it is, Cordelia.
          That's why we're here. Capiche?

                    CORDELIA
          Capiche? Like you're Mr. World
          Traveler.

Willow enters, joins them.

                    BUFFY
          Where's Giles? I know he'd hate to
          miss this.

                                                      CONTINUED

26 CONTINUED: 26

                         WILLOW
               He said we should get started and
               he'd be by as soon as possible.

Xander hands Buffy a small scalpel.

                         XANDER
               So. Okay. Get started Buffy.
               Dissect it or something.

                         BUFFY
               Dissect it? Why me?

                         XANDER
               You're the Slayer.

                         BUFFY
               I slayed! My work here is done.

She hands the scalpel back to Xander.

                         XANDER
               Oh no. I almost ate one of these
               things. I've fulfilled my gross-out
               quota for the decade.

                         WILLOW
               Guys?

She takes the scalpel. Cuts. Some BLUE GOOD SPURTS. Buffy,
Xander and Cordy all react.

                         XANDER
               Do we have any idea what to look for?
               I mean, how are we supposed to figure
               out what this thing is?

                         BUFFY
               Turn it over. Maybe we missed its
               I.D. bracelet.

CLOSE ON CORDELIA'S BACKPACK

Unbeknownst to all, the BEAR undulates slightly. Little cub
paws and legs writhing.

CLOSER STILL ON BACKPACK

One of the teddy bear's EYES starts to push out from its
socket. It gives and POPS off. As does the other one. Two
HAIRY TENDRILS EMERGE from the eyes and WORM DOWN CORDELIA'S
BACK.

                                                        CONTINUED

26 CONTINUED: (2)   26

     ON BUFFY, ET AL

                    XANDER
          So now I guess we know what happened
          to Mr. Whitmore.

                    CORDELIA
          He saw one of these things and ran
          away?

                    BUFFY
          Try - best case scenario.

                    WILLOW
          It's possible that Mr. Whitmore
          wasn't harmed. Maybe the offspring
          simply used him to return to the
          mother Bezoar.

                    XANDER
          Yeah. Maybe he--
               (then/to Willow)
          What?

                    BUFFY
          What's a Bezo--

     But before Buffy can finish asking the question, CORDELIA
     BLIND SIDES her with a lead pipe.

                    BUFFY (cont'd)
          Hey!

     She drops.

                    XANDER
          Cordy! What--

     He turns just in time to see an expressionless WILLOW, about
     to bring a heavy microscope down on his head.

27 INT. JANITOR'S CLOSET - DAY   27

     Buffy and Xander are dragged in by their friends, who leave
     and shut the door.

28 INT. SCHOOL HALLWAY - DAY   28

     Willow and Cordelia lock the door. The both have the same
     distant stares. The same "zombie" body-language.

                                                          CONTINUED

28 CONTINUED: 28

Without a word, they start down the hall, joining other
students and teachers who are similarly afflicted.

CLOSE ON ONE OF THE STUDENTS

We see the now familiar tentacles boring into his back at the
base of his spine.

29 EXT./INT. GROUNDSKEEPER'S SHED - DAY   29

The door opens and Willow enters, grabs an axe. Cordy and
others follow, grabbing picks, hoes -- any thing you can dig
with.

30 INT. HALL OUTSIDE BOILER ROOM - DAY   30

They head for the door.

31 INT. BOILER ROOM - DAY   31

They go down the stairs and into the room. They file into
the hole and disappear. Whitmore stands by the hole, even
dirtier than before, watching them enter.

32 EXT. SCHOOL - NIGHT   32

To establish.

33 INT. LIBRARY - NIGHT   33

Joyce enters the library. It appears to be empty.

                    JOYCE
              Buffy? Hello?

Giles emerges from his office.

                    GILES
              Hello.

                    JOYCE
              Mr. Giles, hello. I was looking for
              Buffy. She was supposed to wait for
              me here.

                    GILES
              She's not been in. I was waiting to
              talk to her... about history texts.

                                                        CONTINUED

33 CONTINUED: 33

                          JOYCE
          Well, that is just the last straw.

                          GILES
          I'm sure she didn't mean to --

                          JOYCE
          She never means to, but somehow she   *
          always manages to anyway. Do you
          have children, Mr. Giles?
                    (sudden cringe)
          Should I be whispering?

                          GILES
          No, and no I haven't any children.
          Although sometimes I feel as though
          I do. Working here.

                          JOYCE
          They can be such a -- I don't want to
          say burden, but... actually, I kind
          of do want to say burden.

                          GILES
          Feel free.

                          JOYCE
          Burden. Thank you. They're just so
          irresponsible.

                          GILES
          Sometimes...

She notices a couple of books on the counter.

                          JOYCE
          "Bristow's Demon Index"?   "Hell's
          offspring"?

                          GILES
          Hobby of mine. But not having to do
          with Buffy in any way.

He takes the book and goes back behind the counter, dropping
them in a book cart. He appears perplexed, coming back to
Joyce, the counter between them now.

                          GILES (cont'd)
          Buffy told you she'd be here? All
          afternoon?

                          JOYCE
          Well, yes... Is something wrong?

                                                    CONTINUED

                    GILES
          I'm sure it's nothing...

There is a BANG from the hallway -- a door slammed open,
probably. Giles' fur is suddenly up.

                    GILES (cont'd)
          What was that?

                    JOYCE
                (turning to the door)
          Probably the janitor...

Giles puts a creature on the back of her neck. She screams,
falls as it scrambles down under her shirt.

ON GILES

Void of feeling. Watching the thing attack her.

                                        BLACK OUT.

                    END OF ACT THREE

ACT FOUR

34   INT. HALL OUTSIDE LIBRARY - EVENING   34

A couple of zombified students walk past the library. After
a few beats the doors open and Giles and Joyce walk into the
hall, heading down in the same direction.

35   INT. JANITOR'S CLOSET - EVENING   35

Buffy sits up, feeling her head where she was hit. She sees
Xander lying beside her, touches his shoulder.

                    BUFFY
          Xander?

He stirs, groaning. Stays on his back, looking up in a
slight daze.

                    BUFFY (cont'd)
          Are you okay?

                    XANDER
          Man, the last time Cordy dragged me
          in here was a lot nicer...

                    BUFFY
          What?

                    XANDER
          Uh, nothing. Crazy talk. Head
          trauma.

                    BUFFY
             (feels her head)
          Yeah, I'm gonna have a bump...

                    XANDER
             (feeling his)
          I'm gonna have a **peninsula** here.
          What the hell is going on? Cordy,
          and Willow...

                    BUFFY
             (rising)
          Something to do with our hatchlings,
          I'm sure of that.

She tries the door. It's locked. Xander sits up, moving
slowly.

                                                    CONTINUED

35 CONTINUED: 35

                         XANDER
               What are they, possessed?

                         BUFFY
               I don't know. They sure wanted us
               out of the way.

                         XANDER
               Why not kill us? Why drag us in
               here -- oh.

As he says it looks to the side -- and the camera arms down
to reveal two eggs sitting on a crate. As they come into
view, one of them jiggles, making that clicking sound.

                         XANDER (cont'd)
                    (small voice)
               Bad now.

Buffy sees 'em too. Grabs a heavy tool chest and **slams it**
down on top of them. BLUE GOO OOZES out from under the chest.

                         XANDER (cont'd)
                    (schwarzeneggar)
               You're scrambled.

He gets up as Buffy moves back to the door.

                         XANDER (cont'd)
               See, we make a great team. You kill,
               I pun.

Buffy rears back and KICKS the door open.

36 INT. LIBRARY - NIGHT   36

Buffy and Xander enter at a decent clip.

                         BUFFY
               Giles?

                         XANDER
               Giles! He must be out somewhere.

                         BUFFY
               He picked a hell of a time to get a
               life.

                         XANDER
               What do we do?

                                                        CONTINUED

36 CONTINUED: 36

                         BUFFY
              We can't fight these things unless we
              know something about them.

                         XANDER
              Willow said something... a name...
              what was it?

                         BUFFY
              A Bozo! Not a bozo.

                         XANDER
              Bezoar.

                         BUFFY
              Yes! Great. Okay, so, we look it up.

                         XANDER
              In what?

                         BUFFY
              A book?

She crosses to the table, Xander following.

                         BUFFY (cont'd)
              Giles said he was gonna try to find
              something.

Buffy looks at a couple of books open on Giles' desk.

                         BUFFY (cont'd)
              Okay, I'd say he found something.

ANGLE: A BOOK

is open to a picture of an egg creature.

Xander steps up to look and we hear something crunch under
his foot.

                         XANDER
              I'd say something found him.

He points to:

ANGLE: THE BROKEN EGG ON THE FLOOR

Buffy looks at it grimly.

37 INT. BOILER ROOM - NIGHT   37

    Joyce and Giles walk calmly into the boiler room, a couple of
    students a ways ahead. They proceed into the hole.

38 INT. UNDERGROUND CAVE - CONTINUOUS - NIGHT   38

    They come down into a vast (TV-wise), dark tunnel junction.
    Tunnels go off in different directions, abandoned and
    partially caved in. The walls are brick and concrete. The
    floor is a rocky pit, in the process of being dug even deeper
    by the twenty or so people inside. They use picks, rakes,
    shovels -- everything they can find. Among the diggers are
    Willow and Mr. Whitmore.

    ANGLE: CORDELIA

    is with the security guard and a few others. They are
    pulling eggs out of a sort of gooey web in the corner of the
    pit, putting them in crates.

39 INT. LIBRARY - NIGHT   39

    Buffy is reading, talking.

                    BUFFY
            A pre-prehistoric parasite... the
            mother hibernates underground, laying
            eggs. Offspring attach themselves to
            a host, taking control of their motor
            functions through neural clamping.

                    XANDER
            Neural clamping? That sounds
            skippable.

                    BUFFY
            So our people are taking orders from
            the mama Bezoar. Which begs the
            question --

                    XANDER
            -- What does mommy want?

    there is a SCREAM from outside.

                    JOHNATHAN (O.S.)
            Ahhh! Get it off me! Get it off!

    The two rush out into the hall, run to the nearby stairs.

    JOHNATHAN on the staircase. As Buffy and Xander approach, he
    gets up, suddenly calm.

                                                        CONTINUED

39 CONTINUED: 39

                         BUFFY
               Are you all right?

                         JOHNATHAN
               Yes, I'm fine. I slipped.

He moves past them, smiling blandly. Walks down the hall.

                         BUFFY
               I think I hear mommy calling...

Xander nods. They follow, at a discreet distance.

40 INT. BOILER ROOM - NIGHT   40

They enter, still making with the calm. Johnathan disappears
down the hole. They pause.

                         XANDER
               Do we really wanna go in there?

                         BUFFY
               We really don't.

They follow.

41 INT. UNDERGROUND CAVE - CONTINUOUS - NIGHT   41

They come out to see the digging. They stay in the tunnel
entrance, in the shadows. They whisper:

                         XANDER
               What are they digging up?

Buffy looks closely, sees:

ANGLE: HOLE IN THE GROUND

As two Zombies haul off a broken chunk of rock, widening the
small hole the diggers have made. Just within the hole we
can see a piece of the MOTHER BEZOAR, a slimy expanse of back
that moves and breathes below the cave.

                         BUFFY
               Oh, boy...

Xander looks around further, nudges Buffy. Points.

ANGLE: THEIR POV OF CORDELIA

As she takes a crate load of eggs and heads down a dark
tunnel.

                                                            CONTINUED

41 CONTINUED: 41

                          BUFFY (cont'd)
                We can't let them spread those things.

                          XANDER
                I know. I'll handle it. Can you
                hold the fort? Better yet -- can you
                kill the fort?

                          BUFFY
                I'll try.

Xander moves off after Cordy, becoming very calm and
deliberate in his movements as he skirts past the others. He
disappears into the tunnel.

Buffy watches him go, takes another look at the dig.

                          BUFFY (cont'd)
                I'm gonna need a weapon. I'm gonna
                need a big weapon.

She heads back towards:

42 INT. BOILER ROOM - CONTINUOUS - NIGHT   42

She emerges from the tunnel and walks straight into the
Gorches. They leer at her. She takes a step back.

                          LYLE
                Told you it wasn't over.

                          TECTOR
                She's so cute and little.
                     (turns to Lyle)
                Can we keep her?

                          BUFFY
                Guys, this is not a great time.

                          LYLE
                It's **gonna** be.

They both rush her -- which she expects. She parries, sends
Tector flying back on his ass. Lyle hurls himself at her and
they both go flying into the hole --

43 INT. UNDERGROUND CAVE - CONTINUOUS - NIGHT   43

and into the cave, rolling right into the midst of the zombie
throng.

They land a bit apart. Lyle stands, bewildered.

                                                          CONTINUED

43 CONTINUED: 43

                          LYLE
               What the hell is this?

Buffy stands -- and finds herself face to face with her
mother. Willow looks up from her digging --

                          BUFFY
               Mom?

                          WILLOW
               Kill them.

Mom swings a pickaxe at Buffy -- who clocks it, backing off.

Lyle fends off others, also backing up. He and Buffy end up
back to back, fending off all and sundry.

                          LYLE
               What's going on?

                          BUFFY
               Long story!

She pushes away a teacher as Lyle knocks someone out. In a
moment of brief respite they turn to each other -- and start
trading blows.

Then more zombies attack and they get back to business.

44 INT. TUNNEL - CONTINUOUS - NIGHT   44

Cordy walks along, one other zombie trailing a bit behind.
He stops, listening. Turns back.

Xander grabs his head and SLAMS it into the brick wall of the
tunnel. The guy is out.

Cordy places her eggs on the floor and comes at Xander. He
weaves away from a punch --

                          XANDER
               Cordelia, I don't want to hurt you...
               some of the time...

He makes for the eggs and she gets in a glancing blow to the
head. He doubles over in major pain.

                          XANDER (cont'd)
               OW! That's my **bump**!

He uppercuts her into unconsciousness -- remorse following
hard on the swing.

                                                    CONTINUED

44 CONTINUED: 44

                           XANDER (cont'd)
            Sorry...

45 INT. UNDERGROUND CAVE - CONTINUOUS - NIGHT   45

Tector emerges from the hole, furious.

                           TECTOR
              Where is that sorry-ass girl?

He stops, looking at the tableau of digging and fighting.
Buffy and Lyle have reaches high ground, at the entrance of
a caved-in tunnel, and the zombies are just eyeing them,
focussing on containment.

Before he has time to register all this, someone comes up
next to him. It's Giles.

Giles hits him in the back of the head with the flat end of
an axe. He goes flying, landing on his belly with his face
right over the hole. The Bezoar moving right below his face.

                           TECTOR (cont'd)
              What is that....?

An eye opens right below him.

A tentacle shoots out and wraps around his head. He is
pulled into the hole before he has time to scream.

ANGLE: BUFFY AND LYLE

Stop to look -- horror on Lyle's face -- and listen, as
somewhere down below, Tector finally finds the moment to
scream.

                           LYLE
              Tector! TECTOR!!!

The scream finally dies, replaced by chomping sounds. Lyle
turns on Buffy.

                           LYLE (cont'd)
              This is all your fault!

                           BUFFY
            How?

But he grabs her and throws her down toward the hole. She
lands hard.

                                                      CONTINUED

45 CONTINUED: 45

Tentacle comes up and wraps around her feet. She looks down
at her feet -- then up at her mother, who swings the pickaxe
down at her face!

Buffy rolls as the axe is buried in the ground next to her
head. She grabs hold of it -- and the tentacle yanks her
toward the hole. Buffy strains to hold onto the axe -- but
it pulls free from the rock and Buffy falls into the hole
holding it.

For a moment we hear nothing.

Then we hear a grunt of effort and the very definite SQUISH
of an axe going into flesh. Then a SCREAM no human could
make.

ANGLE: LYLE

listening to the fight-- the axe going in again and again.

ANGLE: WILLOW AND THE OTHERS

stand and listen as well. A final dying scream and we see:

ANGLE: THE SMALL OF WILLOW'S BACK

As the creature on it dies and slumps to the ground.

Willow blinks, dazed, then sinks to ground in a dead faint.
Lyle watches as everyone else does the same. For a sec
nothing is moving in here.

ANGLE: THE HOLE

A hand -- another -- and Buffy pulls herself out of the hole.
She is covered in blue gunk. And looks about as deadly
pissed about that fact as a human can be.

Lyle stares back at her for all of three seconds before he
runs away, calling out behind him:

                    LYLE
          Okay, it's over now...

And he's gone.

46 EXT. SCHOOL - NIGHT   46

Xander and Giles are helping people out of the building.
Giles is still a little groggy.

                                                    CONTINUED

                              GILES
                    Yes, it was a gas leak, just get some
                    air and you'll all be fine...
                              (to Xander)
                    What really happened?

                              XANDER
                    Go with Gas leak. I'll fill you in
                    later.

He crosses to Willow and Cordelia.

                              XANDER (cont'd)
                    How're you guys doing?

                              WILLOW
                    Did I really hit you?

                              XANDER
                    Knocked me out.

                              CORDELIA
                    Did I hit you?

                              XANDER
                    Yes, everybody hit me.

                              CORDELIA
                    Oh, good. I mean, not good that I
                    hit you, but... I didn't want to be
                    left out.

Buffy walks by, freshly scrubbed and in gym clothes. Passing
Xander she asks:

                              BUFFY
                    Is she all right?

                              XANDER
                    Fine. Little confused. It's going
                    around.

Buffy proceeds to the object of their discussion -- Joyce.

                              BUFFY
                    Hey, mom, are you doing okay?

                              JOYCE
                    Buffy! I was worried you might have
                    gotten caught in the building. There
                    was a gas leak.

CONTINUED

46 CONTINUED: (2)   46

                    BUFFY
          I just heard. I was working out. In
          the gym.

                    JOYCE
          I went looking for you in the library.

                    BUFFY
          Oh, yeah, well, I was gonna be there
          but --

                    JOYCE
          I thought I made it pretty clear you
          weren't to leave the library till I
          arrived.

                    BUFFY
          True, but the other side of that is --

                    JOYCE
          I'm not really interested in the
          other side right now. You have got
          to learn some responsibility, young
          lady. Once and for all.

                    BUFFY
          I'm grounded?

                    JOYCE
          You're already grounded.

                    BUFFY
          Oh yeah.

                    JOYCE
          Until further notice, you're confined
          to you room. You will not leave your
          room at any time except to go to
          school or the bathroom. Your meals
          will be brought to you -- and they
          will not be very good. Am I making
          myself clear?

                    BUFFY
          You're clear. I'll stay in my room.

                    JOYCE
          Damn right you will.

47 EXT. BY A TREE - NIGHT   47

    ANGLE: BUFFY AND ANGEL CLOSE UP

Buffy and Angel are in midsmootch, much heat between them.
After a suitable time they stop, Angel saying:

                  ANGEL
        You sure you're not gonna get in
        trouble?

                  BUFFY
        Hey, I earned this. Besides, I'm not
        breaking any rules.

She kisses him again, and we hear:

                JOYCE (O.S.)
        Buffy, are you going to bed?

The CAMERA pulls back to reveal that BUFFY IS IN HER ROOM --
and Angel is on the roof outside her window, where they kiss.

                  BUFFY
        In a minute, mom...

They get back to it.

                        BLACK OUT.

                THE END